THE AMAZING ADVENTURES OF FLASH GORDON

VOLUME ONE

tempo books
GROSSET & DUNLAP
A Filmways Company
Publishers • New York

THE AMAZING ADVENTURES OF FLASH GORDON,
Volume One

ISBN: 0-448-17349-2
A Tempo Books Original
Tempo Books is registered in the U.S. Patent Office
Published simultaneously in Canada
Printed in the United States of America

ENTER THE AMAZING WORLD OF FLASH GORDON

Flash Gordon has graced newspaper comics pages since 1934. Flash is still with us—constantly thrilling his public with astounding adventures—in Outer Space, here on Earth, even back on Mongo where it all began.

In this volume you will meet old and dear friends—like Dale Arden and Hans Zarkov. You will also meet the Dahlmeister, a brilliant scientist who attempts to control the world with his miniature Army. And Queen Undina, Flash's nemesis from the Water World of Mongo, is back and causing more trouble than ever.

There's action, adventure and suspense here for you to enjoy when you enter the AMAZING WORLD OF FLASH GORDON.

FLASH GORDON in ADVENTURE IN GREECE

A malfunctioning Time-Hopper has deposited Flash and Vicki in a time and place far removed from their own...

FIRST, THERE'S A CITY... THEN, RUINS... AND NOW, A DIFFERENT CITY!
WHAT DOES IT MEAN, FLASH?

THE TIME-HOPPER IS ON THE BLINK, VICKI!

WHERE ARE WE, FLASH?
THE CAMP OF THE GREEK ARMY THAT LAY SIEGE TO TROY!
WE'VE GONE WAY BACK TO THE YEAR 1200 BC, VICKI!

MORE PRISONERS, ACHILLES?
THEY WERE BEHIND OUR LINES, MY KING! SPIES!
ACHILLES?! AND KING..

..AGAMEMNON! YOU ARE KING AGAMEMNON OF MYCENAE AND CORINTHIA!
YOU KNOW ME, TROJAN?! HOW?!

HE SPOKE MY NAME, TOO, MY KING OF KINGS!
AND THOSE OF ALL OUR GENERALS! I LIKE IT NOT!
JUST HEAR ME OUT!

...I AM NOT A TROJAN, SON OF ATREUS! I AM SENT BY THE ORACLE OF APOLLO HIMSELF!
ANOTHER CRACKPOT PROPHET?! I HAVE HAD MY BELLYFUL OF PROPHESIES!
© King Features Syndicate, Inc., 1974. World rights reserved.

LET ME FINISH HIS PRATTLING HERE AND NOW, MY LORD!
THEN YOU SHALL NOT HEAR HOW THE WAR WILL BE WON!

HOLD, ACHILLES! I WISH TO HEAR THIS!
ULYSSES ?!

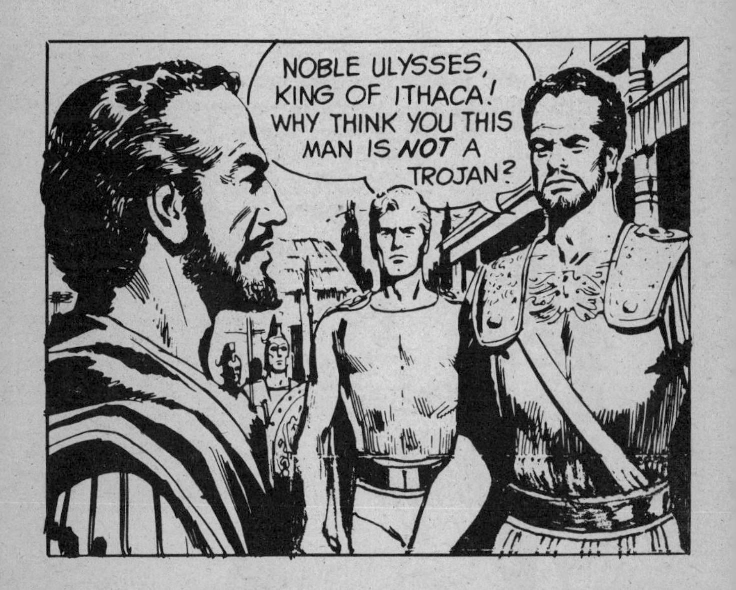
NOBLE ULYSSES, KING OF ITHACA! WHY THINK YOU THIS MAN IS NOT A TROJAN?

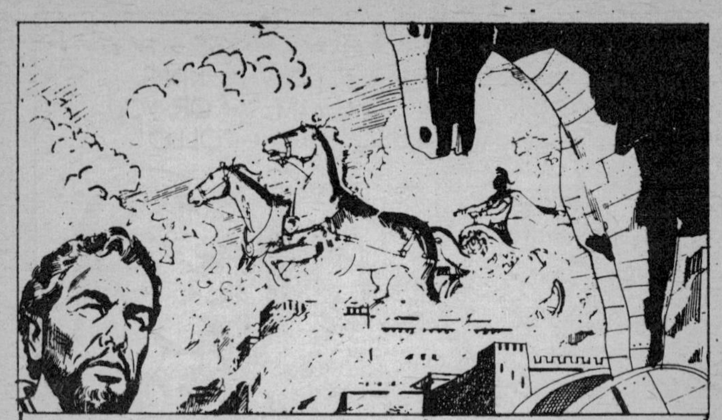

ULYSSES RELATES HIS VISIONS! A CHARIOT DESCENDING FROM OLYMPUS... A GIANT HORSE ON WHEELS... AND THE CITY OF TROY IN FLAMES!

I AM NOT CONVINCED BY DREAMS! IF YOU GO TO FIND THE CHARIOT... SHE STAYS... AS A HOSTAGE!
AS A HOSTAGE— NOT YOUR SLAVE, KING AGAMEMNON! OR YOU ANSWER TO APOLLO!

ULYSSES AGREES TO ACCOMPANY FLASH!
'CHARIOT'? FLASH MEANS THE TIME-HOPPER!
AND I HOPE HE FINDS IT FAST!
12/8

AT THE SPOT WHERE FLASH HAD LEFT THE TIME-HOPPER...
NOTHING HERE! YET IT COULD NOT BE MOVED WITH-OUT HORSES!

ULYSSES! SEE THOSE TRACKS? IT WAS TOWED AWAY!

...TO THAT BARGE! THE TROJANS HAVE IT!
BY NOW IT IS WITHIN THE WALLS OF TROY, GORDON!

IT IS A CHARIOT OF THE GODS! WE *MUST* GET IT BACK!
IMPOSSIBLE!

THE CHARIOT IS LOST - UNTIL THE WAR IS WON!
FOR TEN YEARS WE HAVE NOT BREACHED THOSE MIGHTY WALLS!

WELL, THAT'S WHAT I'M HERE FOR! TO HELP YOU GET THE WAR WON!
YOU CAN DO THAT?! HOW?
BY GETTING YOU INSIDE THOSE WALLS!
12/15

FLASH DECIDES TO GIVE HISTORY A HELPING HAND WHEN THE TIME-HOPPER FALLS INTO TROJAN HANDS!

AHAHAHA!
AN ARMY... INSIDE A WOODEN HORSE!
EEE-HA! OOOHOOO HAAA--
THAT IS YOUR DREAM PLAN?!

NOT AN ARMY... ONLY A PATROL, AGAMEMNON! TO GET INTO THE CITY..
AND OPEN THE GATES TO TROY!

WHICH YOU- IN TEN YEARS— HAVE FAILED TO DO!
MY OWN TROOPS SHALL CARRY OUT HIS PLAN!
?! YOU ARE SERIOUS, ULYSSES!

A SIGN FROM THE GODS IS ALWAYS SERIOUS! YOU MAY YET LEARN THAT!

I LIKE IT NOT, ACHILLES! MY GREAT GENERAL IS LIKE A CALF UNTO THIS GORDON!
HOW MUCH 'GOD' IS HE, IF YOU CAPTURED HIM WITHOUT A STRUGGLE?
I WONDERED ON THAT ALSO, SIRE!
©King Features Syndicate, Inc., 1974. World rights reserved.

DEAR ACHILLES! BRAVE... AND NOT TOO BRIGHT!
THEN TEST HIM, ACHILLES!

MY PLEASURE, SIRE!
12/22

ACHILLES HAS CHALLENGED THE MAN NAMED GORDON! BUT ULYSSES FORBADE BLOODSHED!
THEY ARE TO BE PITTED ON THE GAME FIELD!

A DREAM MATCH! FLASH GORDON VS. ACHILLES!
TOO BAD THERE'S NO TV COVERAGE!
YOU FIRST, ACHILLES.

WHOOO!
85 METERS! ACHILLES HAS BESTED HIS OWN RECORD!
THAT'S LESS THAN 300 FT.! I DID BETTER IN COLLEGE!

BUT I CAN'T MAKE THEIR HERO LOOK LIKE A BUM! SO...

FLASH PUTS HIS JAVELIN RIGHT WHERE HE WANTS IT!
AMAZING! HE HIT THE SAME SPOT!

IN EACH EVENT FLASH JUST EQUALS THE GREAT GREEK HERO.
IF I BEST HIM, THAT CROWD WILL HATE ME...

...AND I NEED THEM TO GET ME INTO TROY!
NO STANDOFF IN THIS EVENT, GORDON! WE FIGHT TILL ONE MAN FALLS!

ACHILLES...UNEQUALED IN MAN-TO-MAN BATTLE... NOW FACES FLASH GORDON...

...AND GETS A LESSON IN THE ART OF MODERN BOXING!

BOOOOOO!
IS THIS A BATTLE OR A BALLET?

THEY WON'T SETTLE FOR A DRAW!
SORRY, PAL...

...I'VE GOT TO WIN THOSE BOYS OVER TO MY SIDE!
FLASH UNLOADS A HAYMAKER...

..BUT SLIPS!
IMPOSSIBLE! ACHILLES IS DOWN!
SO IS GORDON!
ANOTHER STAND-OFF!

FLASH HAS PROVEN SOMETHING TO THE GREEKS - AND TO HIMSELF...
... HE IS THE EQUAL OF THE LEGENDARY ACHILLES.

WITH ACHILLES' SUPPORT, FLASH'S PROJECT QUICKLY TAKES SHAPE.

AND SOON...
IT IS READY, ULYSSES!
SO ARE MY TROOPS!

AT DAWN... THE SENTRIES ON THE WALLS OF TROY ARE GREETED BY AN INCREDIBLE SIGHT...

IT IS SOME TRICK OF THE WILY GREEKS!
IT SHOULD BE BURNED, PRINCE HECTOR!
NO! IT IS ANOTHER OMEN!

THE PUZZLING NEWS SPREADS THROUGHOUT TROY!
DID THE GODS NOT SEND THIS WONDROUS CHARIOT TO US?
THE GREEKS HAVE NOT ATTACKED US SINCE THEN!

1/19
NOW THEY SEND A MIGHTY HORSE TO PULL THAT CHARIOT! IT IS A SIGN FOR VICTORY!

WHILE INSIDE THE HORSE...
WE ARE MOVING, GORDON!
YES, ULYSSES! THEY'VE OPENED THE GATES!!

THIS GIFT IS A SIGN FROM ABOVE, KING PRIAM! TOMORROW WE MARCH!

BUT AS TROY SLEEPS...

AFTER TEN BITTER YEARS. THE GATES TO TROY ARE OPENED!
THE REST IS HISTORY! TIME FOR MY EXIT!

BUT THE PLUNDERING GREEKS REACH THE TIME-HOPPER FIRST!
TROJAN JUNK! WRECK IT!
1/26

THE GREEK SOLDIERS SACK TROY... LOOTING AND WRECKING AS THEY GO!
THEY DESTROYED THE TIME-HOPPER!

CHEER UP, GORDON! THE GODS WILL REWARD YOU WITH ANOTHER CHARIOT!
NOT LIKE THIS ONE, ULYSSES!

FLASH FINDS VICKI AT THE TROJAN PALACE..
FLASH! LOOK AT THIS PAD! MINE! YOU RATE ...
AND, I'M WITH YOU!
VICKI.. BAD NEWS! WE'RE STRANDED HERE!

THE TIME-HOPPER IS TOTALLY WRECKED!
WE'LL NEVER GET BACK NOW!

THAT'S BAD? WE'RE GODS HERE! JEWELS, SERVANTS! KING AGGIE AT MY FEET!
THAT YUMMY GUY, ACHILLES, AFTER ME...

WHO WANTS TO LEAVE?
IF WE DON'T FOUL HISTORY ANY MORE THAN WE HAVE..
..THEY WILL BOTH BE DEAD SOON!

NO!?
YES! AND THERE'S NOTHING IN THE BOOKS ON WHAT HAPPENS TO US!!
HOW DOES THAT HIT YOU?

SO THE TIME-HOPPER IS GONE! MAKE THE BEST OF IT, FLASH...
EVEN WITHOUT TV AND CENTRAL HEATING...

...LIFE DOESN'T LOOK BAD- FROM INSIDE A PALACE!
VICKI! AM I SEEING THINGS?

FLASH! ARE YOU CRAZY?!
DON'T JUMP, PLEASE!

BUT FLASH LANDS ON THE TERRACE BELOW...
HERE! OVER HERE!
© King Features Syndicate, Inc., 1975. World rights reserved.

LOOK!
ANOTHER TIME-HOPPER OUT OF THE FUTURE!

WE'VE CROSSED 40 CENTURIES TO RESCUE YOU, FLASH GORDON!
NOW WE MUST BE OFF!
WAIT! VICKI...

GO AHEAD, FLASH...
I'M STAYING ... WITH ACHILLES!
VICKI... YOU CAN'T! YOU MUSTN'T!

WHY NOT? BECAUSE IT'S NOT IN THE HISTORY BOOKS?
MAYBE THE *BOOKS* ARE WRONG... MAYBE *WE'VE* CHANGED THEM ALREADY!

SORRY! WE CANNOT LINGER!
I HOPE YOU'RE RIGHT, VICKI! GOOD LUCK!

WILL ULYSSES WANDER FOR TEN YEARS? WILL ACHILLES DIE BY AN ARROW IN HIS HEEL?
HE DIDN'T KILL HECTOR ...AS LEGEND CLAIMS!

I'LL NEVER KNOW!
WE'RE COMING INTO THE 20TH CENTURY! YOU ARE HOME AGAIN, FLASH GORDON!
2/16

FLASH GORDON in THE RETURN OF THE DAHLMEISTER

Flash Gordon is reported missing! What World Space Control doesn't know is that Flash has been kidnapped. Gordon escapes his first captors only to be nabbed by a second, more deadly crew...

WORLD SPACE REGIONAL H.Q., ITALY...
ANOTHER MESSAGE FROM AN ADRIATIC FISHING BOAT...
THEY'VE FOUND FLASH GORDON, TOO?

GET THIS! WE CAN HAVE HIM FOR 3 MILLION DOLLARS!
RANSOM? THE OTHERS ONLY CLAIMED REWARDS!

I GUESS WE ADD IT TO THE LIST!
RIGHT! THAT MAKES ONLY 183 CRACKPOT CLAIMS FOR THE RESEARCH TEAM TO CHECK OUT!

LUBO! THAT BOAT! THEY FISHED SOMEONE OUT!
IT MUST BE HIM!

THEY'VE GOT FLASH GORDON! THIEVES! HE'S OUR HOSTAGE!
HA-HA-HA! YES, HE WAS...
© King Features Syndicate, Inc., 1975. World rights reserved.

...AND YOUR RADIO RANSOM MESSAGE LED US RIGHT TO HIM!
THANKS, FISHERMEN!

GREGOR GABORSK HAS PLANS FOR MR. GORDON!
BIG PLANS! EH, FABIAN?

HA-HEE-HEE! YES! GIANT PLANS, COMRA... UH... MASTER GREGOR!

HE IS RESTING NICELY, MASTER GREGOR!
GOOD, GOOD! KEEP HIM UNDER SEDATION UNTIL I AM READY!

WHAT A DREAM! FLASH GORDON! A PERFECT COMPANION FOR MY *FIRST* CREATION!
BY THE WAY, FABIAN! HOW IS NATASHA?

RESTLESS, MASTER! SHE'S BENT HER BARS AGAIN!

A REMOTE CASTLE IN TRANSYLVANIA...
IT'S STARTING, MASTER GREGOR!

A THUNDER-STORM! SEND UP THE ANTENNA, FABIAN!
ANTENNA GOING UP, MASTER!

HERE IT COMES!

HA-HA! NOW FLASH GORDON WILL BECOME MY SECOND SUPER-BEING!

HIS MIND... HIS GREAT PHYSICAL POWER...
...ALL SCALED UPWARD TO GIANT PROPORTIONS!

TWO SUPER-BEINGS! BOTH SERVING GREGOR GABORSK! THE WORLD WILL ACCLAIM ME!
MASTER! IT... IT'S NATASHA!

SHE'S BROKEN HER CELL BARS..
NATASHA! AWAY FROM THERE! IT IS I, YOUR MASTER!

I COMMAND YOU! STOP!
ST... MMFFF!
4/6

NATASHA! COME BACK!

WE MUST FIND THEM! NATASHA HAS GONE BERSERK!
WHAT WENT WRONG, MASTER? SHE USED TO OBEY YOU!

THE LIGHTNING! PANIC BROKE THE SPELL... JUST AS I WAS MAKING A *MATE* FOR HER!
THAT'S THE WAY... EVEN WITH SUPER-PEOPLE! NO GRATITUDE!

BEAUTIFUL! JUST BEAUTIFUL!
FLASH GORDON THEY CALLED HIM! NICE!

IT IS GOOD
TO HAVE A FRIEND
AGAIN!

LUBOSH! LOOK!
MERCY! WHAT IS IT?

IT'S AN AMAZON! A KILLER!
I'LL GET HER!

FOOLS! EMPTY-HEADED FOOLS!

WHY? WHY MUST ALL MY GREAT EXPERIMENTS RUN INTO BAD LUCK?
MASTER!

MASTER GREGOR! THE VILLAGERS ARE HUNTING FOR NATASHA! SHE KILLED A PEASANT... WOUNDED ANOTHER!
FOOLS!

THEY PROVOKED HER! WE MUST FIND HER FIRST, FABIAN!
I'LL SHOW YOU WHERE IT HAPPENED, MASTER!

WHILE- IN AN ABANDONED BARN...
AH, FLASH GORDON... YOU AWAKEN! THANK HEAVENS!
?!

YOU ARE PUZZLED, FLASH GORDON? YES, YOU ARE AWAKE!
I AM NOT PART OF A BAD DREAM!

YOU WERE DRUGGED! GABORSK WAS GOING TO MAKE A GIANT OF YOU... AS HE DID TO ME!
GABORSK?

GREGOR GABORSK? THAT MADMAN! HOW?
YOU KNOW HIM! HAVE NO FEAR! NATASHA WILL PROTECT YOU!

THE TRAIL IS CLEAR!
THE GIANT IS IN THERE!

WE KNOW YOU ARE IN THERE!

COME OUT, MURDERESS!
WHAT'S THAT ALL ABOUT, NATASHA?
IDIOT PEASANTS! THEY ATTACKED AT GUN-POINT... AND DIED FOR IT!

NOW THEY ARE ALL RIGHTEOUS OUTRAGE! HYPOCRITES!
LET ME TALK TO THEM! HELP ME UP...
OHH... MY BACK!

VERY WELL! WE **BURN** HER OUT!

YOU MUST HAVE HAD A BAD BLOW– BUT NATASHA IS AN EXPERT IN THESE MATTERS!
OOO! EASY!

SORRY! I FORGET! THAT SWINE GREGOR!
HOW DID IT HAPPEN? WHY DID HE **CHOOSE YOU?**

YOU SEE, FLASH GORDON? THIS IS WHAT THEY WANT!

THE *DOORS* ARE OPENING! GET HER AS SHE COMES OUT!

BUT...
LOOK OUT! RUN!

MY POOR FRIEND, FLASH... WE MUST GET YOU WELL!
NOW ON TO

AT THE REAR OF THE BARN...
NATASHA WILL GET YOU TO SAFETY, FRIEND FLASH!
THIS WAY! THE MONSTER ESCAPES!

ELUDING THE PEASANT MOB, NAT
NOW TENDS TO FLASH.
THERE... THIS WILL STRETCH YOUR SPINE... EASE THE PAIN! BETTER?

HA! YOU DON'T KNOW ME?

I AM NATASHA PETROFF! DOES THAT MEAN ANYTHING?
OF COURSE! OLYMPIC GOLD MEDALS IN FIVE EVENTS!
SIX!

...PRIZE WINNING PHYSICIST... WORLD CHESS CHAMPION! THAT'S WHY GABORSK DID *THIS* TO ME!
AND WOULD HAVE DONE TO YOU...
IF YOU HAD NOT STOPPED HIM!

YES, HE WANTED TO CREATE SUPER BEINGS TO SERVE HIM!
NOW HE MUST BE MADE TO PAY... *DEARLY!*

VERY GOOD, FLASH! YOU ARE RECOVERING BEAUTIFULLY!
THANKS TO YOU, NATASHA!

RUSSIAN INTELLIGENCE... BUDAPEST OFFICE.
THREE MONTHS HAVE NARROWED DOWN CLUES AND SUSPECTS...
NOW OSCAR THE SUPER-BRAIN DIGESTS ALL THE FACTS...

...AND COMES UP WITH THIS!
NATASHA PETROFF—OUR SOVIET SUPER-STAR—WAS KIDNAPPED BY THE MADMAN, GREGOR GABORSK! COME, BORIS!

BUT WHY, SERGEI? HE ALWAYS WORKED FOR US!
HE WORKED ONLY FOR GREGOR GABORSK! THERE! HIS HIDEAWAY!

IF NATASHA IS HERE, WE WILL FIND HER!

BUT GREGOR IS OUT ON HIS OWN SEARCH...
THE TRANS-MITTER IMPLANTED IN NATASHA'S SKIN IS WORKING LOUD AND CLEAR!

AHA! I AM ZEROED IN! SHE IS JUST BELOW US!
READY WITH THE SLEEP GUN, FABIAN?!
READY, MASTER!

OHH!
NATASHA! WHAT IS IT?!

FLASH AND NATASHA ARE CAUGHT IN AN AMBUSH...
FLASH!... RUN! SAVE YOURSELF!

THE SLEEP-PELLET GOT NATASHA! GO AFTER FLASH! HE'S UNARMED!
I'LL GET HIM, MASTER GREGOR!

WANT TO BET?

FABIAN! HURRY IT UP! I NEED A HAND HERE!
CAN *I* HELP?!

NO... FLASH... PLEASE!

D-DON'T SHOOT! I ONLY MEANT TO HELP HER!
GOOD! THEN YOU'LL UNDO WHAT YOU DID TO HER!

REVERSE THE GROWTH PROCESS? IMPOSSIBLE!
NO!
TOO BAD! YOU'LL HAVE TO TELL THAT TO NATASHA.. WHEN SHE COMES TO!

LIAR! YOU HAVE DONE IT... YOU CAN DO IT!
A-HA!

NATASHA - STILL DRUGGED, IS RETURNED TO GREGOR GABORSK'S CASTLE..
REMEMBER, FLASH... I CANNOT GUARANTEE THIS!

IT HAS WORKED WITH ANIMALS! BUT WHETHER I CAN RESTORE NATASHA...
YOU'D BETTER PRAY YOU CAN, GREGOR!

...OR YOU ARE A DEAD MAN!
Y-YES, YES!
FABIAN! SET THE GROW-MACHINE ON REVERSE CYCLE!

NOW... OPEN THE CIRCUITS!
C-CIRCUITS OPEN, MASTER!

WHILE, ABOVE...
IT IS SHE! COMRADE NATASHA!

SOVIET AGENTS WATCH..
FLASH GORDON! SEE, BORIS? THE TRAITOR GABORSK NOW WORKS WITH THEM!
AS YOU FEARED, SERGE! A PROPAGANDA PLOT! WITH NATASHA A PAWN!

THE DOGS! WHAT ARE WE WAITING FOR?
NOT YET, BORIS! WHEN THEIR FIENDISH EXPERIMENT IS DONE... THEN!

YOU DID IT, MASTER! YOU RESTORED HER TO SIZE!
SHE'S COMING TO! DON'T LET HER NEAR ME! PLEASE!

GREGOR HAS REVERSED THE PROCESS WHICH HAD MADE NATASHA INTO A GIANT.
SHE IS COMING TO, MASTER GREGOR!

AS NATASHA AWAKENS...
FLASH?! W-WHAT HAPPENED?! — I'M... CONFUSED...
EASY, NATASHA! YOU'RE OKAY...

GREGOR HAS RESTORED YOU TO NORMAL! IT'S ALL OVER NOW!
GREGOR? GREGOR...?

THEN SUDDENLY THE CLOUD LIFTS...
GREGOR! THE FIEND! THE BEAST!
NATASHA- NO!

NATASHA!
... I CAN'T BUDGE HER!

NATASHA—POSSESSED BY RAGE—HURLS FLASH ASIDE AND ...
THE GUN! HA!

BUT AS FABIAN TAKES AIM...
BANG!
DIE, BOTH OF Y...
© King Features Syndicate, Inc., 1975. World rights reserved.

ON THE ROOFTOP, THE RUSSIAN AGENTS, SERGE AND BORIS...
NATASHA! GOOD GRIEF! SHE'S HIT!
6/1

NATASHA...
IS SHE...?

IT'S ALL RIGHT, FLASH! JUST A FLESH WOUND!
SO YOU FOUND ME, SERGE?
ALMOST TOO LATE, COMRADE NATASHA!

GREGOR IS STILL ALIVE— BUT FABIAN IS DONE FOR!
YOU SAVED OUR LIVES! I WANT TO THANK YOU!
© King Features Syndicate, Inc., 1975. World rights reserved.

HA! THANKS? IT IS GLORY THEY WANT! THAT'S WHY THEY'RE HERE!
TO RETURN NATASHA PETROFF... SOVIET SUPER-STAR... SAFELY HOME!

THAT IS UNFAIR, COMRADE!
I AM NOT YOUR COMRADE, SERGE IVANOVITCH!

MY COUNTRY HAS USED ME! THIS VERMIN, GREGOR GABORSK, HAS USED ME!
NOW IT IS OVER!

I WILL BE NO ONE'S PAWN! I WILL GO OUT THAT DOOR AS A CITIZEN OF THE WORLD!
FAREWELL, SERGE!
NATASHA- YOU CAN'T!

HA! YES I CAN, "COMRADE."
COMING, FLASH?

FOR SOMEONE WHO IS WOUNDED, YOU DO ALL RIGHT, NATASHA!

SERGE'S CHOPPER! CAN YOU FLY ONE, FLASH?
NO PROBLEM, NATASHA!

THERE SHOULD BE A FIRST-AID KIT ABOARD. BETTER SEE TO THAT BULLET WOUND!
GOT IT, FLASH!

NOW...EAST-OR WEST?
I MEANT WHAT I SAID, FLASH! I WILL BE USED BY NEITHER SIDE!

WELL, THERE SEEMS ONLY ONE SOLUTION!
WHAT'S THAT?

YOU COULD JOIN MY OUTFIT.. AND SERVE THE WORLD AT LARGE!
WORLD SPACE CONTROL? YES, PERFECT! I NEVER CONSIDERED IT!
WORLD SPACE CONTROL BALKAN HEADQUARTER

PERHAPS WE MIGHT EVEN BE TOGETHER?
AT BEST OUR PATHS MIGHT CROSS, NATASHA!

WHILE IN ANOTHER PART OF THE WORLD...
AMAZING, PROFESSOR! THEY LOOK ALIVE!
THEY ARE ALIVE, MY DEAR HUGO!

YEARS... IT HAS TAKEN ME YEARS TO START ANEW... BUT I HAVE DONE IT!

REMEMBER, HUGO... I WAS WITHIN *INCHES* OF RULING ALL THE EARTH!
YES, MASTER! YOUR ROBOTS REPLACED THE WORLD'S KEY SCIENTISTS! YOU CONTROLLED EVERYTHING...

... DEFENSE SATELLITES! NUCLEAR BOMBS... WEATHER STATIONS! ALL!
THE WORLD WAS ON ITS KNEES... ITS LEADERS READY TO ACCEPT MY RULE! AND THEN...

... THEY SPOILED IT!
DR. ZARKOV AND FLASH GORDON!

BY MERE ACCIDENT... THEY RUINED THE DREAMS OF A LIFETIME!

YES...THEY DESTROYED MY GRIP ON THE WORLD... AND THOUGHT THEY KILLED ME AS WELL!
HA! THE FOOLS!

LOOK AT MY LATEST CREATIONS! AS LIFELIKE AS ANY HUMAN!
THAT'S WHAT THEY KILLED!
A LIFE-SIZE DUPLICATE OF YOU, PROF. DAHLMEISTER?

EXACTLY! NOW, AFTER YEARS OF WORK... REBUILDING MY PUPPET ARMY.. I AM READY TO HAVE MY REVENGE!

ABOARD AN EARTHBOUND SPACE-LINER...

DALE ARDEN IS RETURNING FROM A VENUS VACATION...
IT HASN'T HELPED ME FORGET FLASH!

WHEN GOOD NEWS REACHES HER–
HAVE YOU HEARD? FLASH GORDON IS ALIVE!
THEY'VE FOUND HIM!

AND I'VE A RADIOGRAM FOR YOU, MISS ARDEN!
EARTHBASE-07382
TIME... 10:2400
DALE DARLING– FINALLY TRACKED YOU DOWN. WILL BE WAITING AT SPACEPORT ON YOUR ARRIVAL.
LOVE FLASH
FLASH! FLASH... AT LAST!

OH- I CAN'T WAIT TO GET THERE!

WHILE, IN THE CONTROL CABIN...

... A GROUP OF TINY UNIFORMED MEN EMEGE FROM THE AIR DUCTS ...

... AND LATER, AT SPACEPORT TRAFFIC TOWER...
HOW'S IT GOING, TERRY?
THIS IS CRAZY, FLASH! THE INBOUND FLIGHT YOU'RE WAITING FOR...
SHE'S REVERSED COURSE... AND IS HEADING BACK OUT INTO SPACE.
6/29

QUIETLY...

NOW WE MUST ALTER THE COMPUTER-NAVIGATOR TAPE!
NEW COORDINATES... 75421... 063...

WHAT'S WRONG? WE'RE MOVING AWAY FROM EARTH!
THE PILOTS' CABIN IS *LOCKED!*

PLEASE STAY SEATED! YOU ARE IN NO DANGER!
THERE HAS BEEN A CHANGE IN FLIGHT PLAN!

AT THE SPACEPORT ON EARTH...
NO RADIO RESPONSE, FLASH! ONLY ONE POSSIBILITY...
A HIJACK! AND DALE IS ABOARD!

DAYS LATER – A MESSAGE COMES THROUGH...
THE PASSENGERS AND SHIP ARE SAFELY LANDED, AS YOU SEE!
THAT'S AN ABANDONED ASTEROID-BASE!

THEY WILL BE RELEASED IF YOU SEND FLASH GORDON AND DR. ZARKOV HERE... ALONE!
DAHLMEISTER!

A ROCKET STREAKS PAST THE RED PLANET MARS...

WE ARE IN THE ASTEROID BELT, ZARKOV!
HERE'S WHERE THE FUN BEGINS...

...THREADING THROUGH THE SMALL STUFF!
WHOOO! STILL WITH ME?

I'M HANGING IN, FLASH! AND THERE'S OUR TARGET... THE BIG ASTEROID UP AHEAD!
OKAY, I'M MATCHING ORBITS!

WE'RE GOING IN!

HOW DO WE HANDLE THIS, FLASH? TURN OURSELVES IN *BEFORE* THEY RELEASE THE HOSTAGES?
THEY'RE HOLDING DALE AND 30-ODD PASSENGERS!

WE CAN'T RISK THEIR LIVES! LET'S JUST SEE WHAT THE SKY-JACKERS WANT WITH US!
FUNNY- NO ONE HERE TO MEET US!

?!

DONE, MASTER!

HA-HA! NOW YOU KNOW HOW GULLIVER FELT!
YOU!?
DAHLMEISTER?

BUT YOU'RE..
I MEAN:...
YOU...
DIED?! YOU
THOUGHT I DID!

YOU FORGET... I
REPLACED YOU
BOTH WITH PERFECT
ROBOT COPIES!
IT WAS NOT
ME YOU SAW
DIE...
...ONLY
A ROBOT!

AND NOW IT IS TIME TO SETTLE OUR ACCOUNTS!

DALE! ARE YOU ALL RIGHT?
SHE'S NEVER BEEN BETTER, FLASH GORDON!

TRUE TO MY WORD, THE PASSENGER SHIP IS BEING RETURNED TO EARTH--
...ALONG WITH THE HOSTAGES!

BUT-ODDLY ENOUGH-IN SPITE OF MY PLEAS--
...MISS ARDEN INSISTS UPON STAYING HERE TO SERVE ME!

A SPACEPORT ON EARTH...
THE HIJACKED SHIP IS BACK SAFELY, BUT FLASH IS STILL OUT THERE

WORLD SPACE CONTROL...
WE CAN'T LEAVE FLASH AND ZARKOV IN THAT MADMAN'S HANDS!
LET ME GET THEM OUT!

WHILE ON AN ASTEROID BEYOND MARS...

BY SERVING ME- AS MISS ARDEN HAS DECIDED TO DO!
CORRECT, MY DEAR?
FAITHFULLY AND DEVOTEDLY, MASTER!

YOU-FLASH GORDON AND DR. ZARKOV- YOU COST ME CONTROL OF THE WHOLE WORLD, ONCE!
NOW YOU CAN HELP SET UP A MODEST LITTLE EMPIRE OUT HERE!

IN RETURN FOR DALE'S FREEDOM?
FREEDOM? HAH! WHAT IS FREEDOM? AN IDEA... A MYTH?

NO, MY FRIENDS, IN RETURN FOR HER LIFE!
AGREED?

WITH DALE UNDER HIS CONTROL, DAHLMEISTER NOW TURNS TO ENSLAVING FLASH AND ZARKOV!
YOU WILL SERVE ME, MY FRIENDS! YOU HAVE NO CHOICE!

MY FIRST PLAN FOR WORLD RULE WAS TOO GRAND! AND SO IT FAILED!
THIS TIME, MY DEAR FLASH AND ZARKOV...

... THIS TIME I SEEK POWER ON A SMALLER SCALE!

HA-HA-HA! A VERY SMALL SCALE INDEED! SEE WHAT I MEAN?

NOW, MY BRAVE ONES! SHALL YOU RESIST ME?
UNTIE MY HANDS AND I'LL ANSWER THAT!

THERE—YOUR BONDS ARE CUT!
I COULD PUT YOUR MINDS UNDER MY SPELL...

BUT IT WILL BE MORE AMUSING TO WATCH YOU STRUGGLE HOPELESSLY!
OHH! THAT DID STING!

HERE, MY FRIENDS! VENT YOUR ANGER ON SOMETHING MORE YOUR SIZE!
A TARANTULA!

ARE WE SUPPOSED TO PANIC, DAHLMEISTER?
HA! HE WON'T ATTACK US OUTSIDE HIS LAIR!

YOU KNOW TARANTULAS, DR. ZARKOV! BUT THIS ONE IS VERY HUNGRY...
...AND HE WILL ATTACK... EVEN OUTSIDE HIS LAIR!
STAND PERFECTLY STILL, FLASH!

HE CAN ONLY LOCATE US IF WE MOVE!
TRUE, TRUE!

BUT YOU WILL MOVE ... WON'T YOU?!

QUICK, FLASH! UP ON ITS BACK!

HAVE YOU HAD ENOUGH OF THIS GAME?
HE CAN'T TOUCH US BACK HERE!
VERY WELL! WE'VE EXPLODED THE *MYTH* ABOUT TARANTULAS!

COME! NOW I WANT YOU TO MEET TABBY!
?!

HA-HA-HE-HA! LOOK AT YOU! IT'S HARD TO BELIEVE...
...YOU TWO ONCE STOOD BETWEEN ME AND WORLD CONQUEST!

COME, FLASH AND ZARKOV! TIME TO MEET ANOTHER OF MY PETS!

LITTLE TABBY! JUST A KITTEN - WHO LOVES TO PLAY!

CAREFUL OF HIS CLAWS! I DON'T WANT YOU DEAD- YET!

HE'S PLAYING CAT AND MOUSE! WAITING FOR US TO RUN! STAY PUT!

HA-HA-HA! YES–I WISH YOU A *LONG* LIFE...
...TO FILL MY IDLE HOURS WITH AMUSEMENT!

BUT THE DOLL-MASTER HAS NEGLECTED DALE, WHO SLOWLY ROUSES FROM HER HYPNOTIC STATE...
© King Features Syndicate, Inc., 1975. World rights reserved.

SUDDENLY HE REMEMBERS... BUT TOO LATE!

DALE'S HEAD SLOWLY CLEARS...
FLASH! ZARKOV! WHERE ARE YOU?
DALE! HERE! HERE!

OH! FLASH? ZARKOV?
I THOUGHT I HEARD SOMETH...

WHAT DID HE DO TO YOU?!
THAT'S EASY TO SEE!

I-I DON'T REMEMBER A BIT OF IT!
YOU WERE UNDER A HYPNOTIC SPELL, DALE!
YOU SNAPPED OUT JUST IN TIME!

DAHLMEISTER WOULD HAVE TORTURED US TO DEATH!
HELP US TRUSS HIM UP BEFORE HE COMES TO!

THERE'S ONLY ONE WAY TO FORCE HIM TO RESTORE US...
THAT IS IF HE CAN!
8/24

BACK OFF, DALE! WE'RE GOING TO GIVE HIM A DOSE OF HIS OWN MEDICINE!

HOW DO YOU FIGURE OUT THESE CONTROLS, ZARKOV?
NOBODY HAS TOUCHED THEM, FLASH! THEY'RE STILL SET!

THIS IS THE SAME BEAM DAHLMEISTER USED ON US! WE'LL BRING HIM DOWN TO OUR SIZE!

IT'S DONE... HE'S COMING TO!
WHAT—WHAT HAPPENED? YOU'VE... GROWN!

NO, DOLL! IT'S THE OTHER WAY 'ROUND!
N-NO! OH, NO!

FLASH, ZARKOV! STAY AWAY! I MEANT YOU NO HARM!
YOU'RE IN DEEP TROUBLE, DAHLMEISTER!

YOU KNOW WHO'S INSIDE HERE? YOUR ARMY OF LITTLE SLAVES!
CLOSE THAT DOOR... PLEASE! IF THEY SEE ME LIKE THIS...

... THEY MIGHT RISE UP AGAINST THEIR MASTER! YOU'VE ONLY ONE CHANCE!
REVERSE THE SHRINKING PROCESS! RESTORE US TO SIZE!

I'VE NEVER WORKED THAT OUT! THE PROCESS CANNOT BE REVERSED!

IT'S... HOPELESS! I KNOW NO WAY TO REVERSE THE SHRINKING PROCESS!

I'M AFRAID WE'RE DOOMED TO BE DWARFED... FOREVER!
NONSENSE, DAHLMEISTER!
DALE...!

HELP US DOWN, WOULD YOU?
YOU'RE GOING TO PILOT US BACK TO EARTH!
I'M... WHAT?!

DON'T WORRY-FLASH WILL DIRECT YOU!
FIRST, THE BUTTON TO THE HANGAR DOOR!
ZARKOV... I'M TERRIFIED!

IT'S OKAY, DALE! I'LL BE RIGHT BESIDE YOU!
YOU CAN DO IT!

TAKEOFF IS NO PROBLEM! THE COMPUTER DOES THE THINKING!
WITH HER THREE DOLL-SIZE PASSENGERS, DALE MANS THE CONTROLS...

I GUESS YOU ARE GOING TO WORK ON AN ANTIDOTE IN YOUR LAB?
HECK, NO, FLASH! REMEMBER NATASHA? THE GIRL WHO TURNED INTO A GIANT?
... WHILE THE PASSENGERS CONSULT.

BY GREGOR GABORSK! YES!
GABORSK?! THAT MADMAN? THAT QUACK? HE USES LIGHTNING... WITCHCRAFT... HE COULD KILL US!
THAT'S WHY YOU'LL GO FIRST, DAHLMEISTER!

UNDER FLASH'S GUIDANCE, DALE PILOTS THEIR SPACESHIP SAFELY BACK TO EARTH

GREGOR GABORSK IS ON FURLOUGH FROM PRISON.
THAT IS MY CASTLE BELOW! WHAT'S THIS ALL ABOUT?
YOU'LL SEE!

FLASH? ZARKOV? AND ISN'T THAT THE MADMAN DAHLMEISTER?
ME, MAD? YOU QUACK! I WILL NOT SUBMIT TO YOUR EXPERIMENT!

YOU DID THIS TO US, DAHLMEISTER!
AND NOW, GREGOR, YOU WILL APPLY THE GABORSK EFFECT TO MAKE US GROW AGAIN!
SO THAT'S IT?!

YOU SENT ME TO PRISON—AND YOU WANT ME TO HELP YOU NOW?! HA!

WE WAITED FOR A STORMY DAY! NOW GET ON WITH IT!
AND IF ANYTHING GOES WRONG... "YOU WERE SHOT TRYING TO ESCAPE!"
UH.. AHH.. AHEM! YES! I GET THE POINT!

LIGHTNING, ARCHAIC TRANSFORMERS...
A MIXTURE OF SORCERY AND SCIENCE...

...THE GABORSK EFFECT IS IN PROGRESS!

FLASH GORDON in RETURN TO THE WATER WORLD OF MONGO

Flash has been summoned to Mongo by Undina, deposed Queen of the Water World of Mongo. The ever-scheming Undina has quite a few surprises in store for her old "friend" Flash Gordon...

QUEEN UNDINA?!
IT'S JUST MIZ UNDINA NOW, FLASH!
SINCE YOU GOT US ONTO SELF-RULE!

YOU'RE STILL GOVERNOR OF THE CORAL KINGDOM?
YES, IN NAME! BUT THERE ARE PROBLEMS... I'M AFRAID ONLY YOU CAN HELP!

WHY ME? WHAT KIND OF PROBLEMS?

THE TRANS-MONGO ALLIANCE HAS A GRIEVANCE COUNCIL! HAVE YOU CONTACTED PRINCE BARIN?
HE CAN'T HELP! THIS IS INTERNAL POLITICS... AND I'M ... DESPERATE!

YOU MUST COME, FLASH! PLEASE...
MMF!
© King Features Syndicate, Inc., 1975. World rights reserved.

ZARKOV! RAISE PRINCE BARIN! IF HE GIVES THE WORD...
...OUR ROCKET IS TUNED AND READY!
9/21

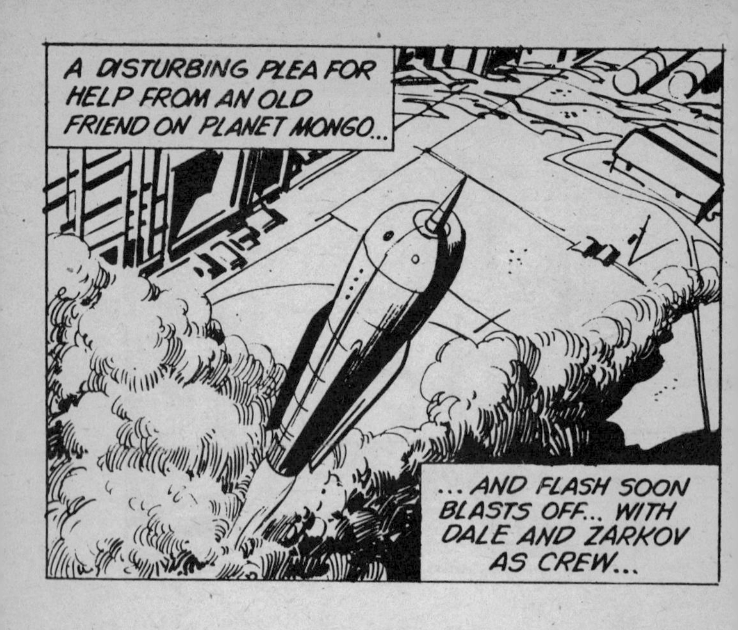
A DISTURBING PLEA FOR HELP FROM AN OLD FRIEND ON PLANET MONGO...
...AND FLASH SOON BLASTS OFF... WITH DALE AND ZARKOV AS CREW...

ALL SYSTEMS GREEN, FLASH! REST TIME! COMPUTER ALARM WILL WAKE US FOR LANDING!
THANKS, DALE! SEE YOU AT TOUCHDOWN TIME!

A FAST LEAP THROUGH SUBSPACE... AND SOON THE ROCKET IS DOWN ON MONGO...
NICE NAVIGATING, DALE!

A BRIEF REUNION WITH PRINCE BARIN, THEN...
THE EXPLORER SUB'S FITTED AND READY, FLASH!
THANKS, BARIN!
REMEMBER— ANY TROUBLE— AND WE'RE STANDING BY!

WELL, LET'S TAKE HER DOWN!

A DIVE OF 2,000 FEET.
A MIRACLE THE SUB CAN TAKE THE PRESSURE!
NO MIRACLE, DALE! SEE? IT'S GETTING LIGHT! THERE'S THE CITY OF MIRAMAR!
© King Features Syndicate, Inc., 1975. World rights reserved.

THEIR FORCE-FIELD NULLIFIES DEPTH PRESSURE! AND THE SEABED GIVES A NATURAL LIGHT!
FLASH!

9/28
LOOK!

AT QUEEN UNDINA'S REQUEST, FLASH ARRIVES AT HER UNDERSEA KINGDOM ON MONGO...

WE'RE AT THE GATES OF THE CORAL CITY, FLASH!
WHAT DO YOU THINK- DO WE GO RIGHT IN?
I'M BEGINNING TO WONDER WHO'S IN TROUBLE...

QUEEN UNDINA ... OR US! THE WAY SHE WAS CUT OFF THE AIR...
IT WAS ALL TOO PAT, FLASH!
YOU SUSPECT A TRAP, DALE?

TO SATISFY DALE'S SKEPTICISM, FLASH SWIMS AHEAD TO INVESTIGATE...
...WHILE THE SUB WAITS IN HIDING...

BUT, AS FLASH APPROACHES THE CITY OF CORAL...

...HE IS SPOTTED FROM A CONNING TOWER...
IT'S GORDON! WHY WOULD HE LEAVE THE SUB?
HE IS NO FOOL, PLUTON!

HE SUSPECTS! IT DOES NOT MATTER! HE IS HERE!
TAKE HIM!
A PLEASURE, MY QUEEN!

A SUDDEN FURIOUS TIDE SUCKS FLASH THROUGH AN OPENING IN THE CITY'S WALL!
10/5

FLASH CANNOT BREAK FREE OF THE JET STREAM THAT SUCKS HIM INTO A TUNNEL.

THE PRESSURE STREAM SWEEPS FLASH OUT INTO A CHAMBER WITHIN THE CORAL CITY.

WE'LL KEEP HIM IN THIS LUNG SUPPORT FOR NOW!
GET THAT SUB HE CAME IN!
AT ONCE!

WITHIN MOMENTS, THE SUB - WITH DALE AND ZARKOV ABOARD - IS TOWED TOWARD THE CITY BY A POWERFUL FORCE-BEAM!

LET'S GO ABOARD! TAKE THE AIR-BREATHERS... ALIVE!

DALE AND ZARKOV ARE SEIZED.. AND CARRIED INTO CORALLIA IN AIR TANKS..

IN UNDINA'S THRONE ROOM...
NOW...WE HAVE THEM ALL, QUEEN UNDINA! YOUR THREE EARTHLING FRIENDS!
YOU CALLED THEM FOR HELP, DIDN'T YOU?
10
12

ONLY IT'S ME THEY'LL HELP! YOU'LL MARRY ME...AND TURN OVER YOUR THRONE...
...OR WATCH YOUR FRIENDS DROWN BEFORE YOUR EYES!
PLUTON...YOU SEA-SWINE! I WILL SEE YOU DEAD FOR THIS!

PLUTON— YOU TRAITOR!
I?! IT IS YOU, MY QUEEN, WHO TRICKED FLASH INTO COMING HERE!...
FOR YOUR OWN PURPOSES!

NO! FOR MY PEOPLE! WITH TRITON'S 'ACCIDENTAL' DEATH... THEY DEMAND A NEW KING!
AND YOU WOULD GIVE THEM AN EARTHMAN?!

FLASH GORDON *SAVED* US ONCE! HE IS A *HERO* TO OUR PEOPLE!
WHILE *YOU* ARE STILL IN LOVE WITH HIM! CONVENIENT!

I HAVE BEEN SECOND IN COMMAND LONG ENOUGH, MY QUEEN!
I WILL *NOT* NOW SERVE A VILE *AIR*-BREATHER!

YOU WERE GOING TO CONVERT HIM TO A WATER-BREATHER...
...AND FORCE HIM TO MARRY YOU!
ONLY NOW HE IS IN *MY* HANDS!
© King Features Syndicate, Inc., 1975. World rights reserved.

SOLDIERS! I COMMAND YOU! ARREST HIM!
SAVE IT, UNDINA! THEY'RE WITH *ME*!
10/19

NOW – YOU WILL ANNOUNCE OUR IMPENDING MARRIAGE...
..OR THE AIR-BREATHERS DROWN *NOW!*

YOU WILL STAY IN THE CUSTODY OF MY LOYAL TROOPS, DEAR QUEEN...
...UNTIL THE CEREMONY IS ARRANGED!
"LOYAL ?!" HA! THEY SHALL DIE A TRAITOR'S DEATH, ALONG WITH *YOU,* PLUTON!

PLUTON LEADS A HUNTING PARTY TO THE SURFACE... TO GATHER MEAT FOR HIS WEDDING FEAST...

BUT QUEEN UNDINA TAKES STEPS TO ESCAPE THE FORCED MARRIAGE...
YOU WILL USE THESE JEWELS TO BRIBE FLASH GORDON'S GUARDS! THEN...
I KNOW THE REST, MY QUEEN!

A FEW WELL-PLACED BRIBES... AND FLASH IS TURNED OVER TO THE ROYAL PHYSICIAN...
IN AN HOUR HE WILL BE A WATER-BREATHER!

WHEN FLASH COMES FULLY AWAKE... UNDINA IS THERE!
WH...?! NO AIR TANK? UNDINA!
YOU DIDN'T--?
I HAD TO, FLASH! OR PLUTON WOULD HAVE KILLED YOU!

YOU'RE LYING! I OVERHEARD! YOU DID THIS MUTATION TO FORCE ME TO MARRY YOU!
WELL, IT WON'T WORK!
PLEASE, FLASH! WE CAN TALK LATER...
10/26
© King Features Syndicate, Inc., 1975. World rights reserved.

RIGHT NOW, WE MUST ESCAPE THE PALACE!
PLUTON'S RETURNING FROM THE SURFACE! AND IF HE FINDS US... WE'LL BOTH DIE!

I'M NOT LEAVING WITHOUT DALE AND ZARKOV!
THEY'RE SAFE IN THEIR OXY-TANKS, FLASH!
MY MEN HAVE CARRIED THEM OFF INTO HIDING!

HIDING? WHERE?
I'M SORRY, FLASH! THAT MUST BE MY SECRET... UNTIL PLUTON IS DEALT WITH!
YOU DON'T MISS A TRICK, UNDINA!

NOT WHEN MY THRONE IS AT STAKE!
NOW FOLLOW ME.. BY NOW PLUTON HAS DISCOVERED OUR ESCAPE!
WE'LL SETTLE UP LATER!

THIS TUNNEL IS KNOWN ONLY TO THE ROYAL HOUSEHOLD!
FOR SKIPPING OUT IN TIME OF TROUBLE? VERY NOBLE!

A LABYRINTH LEADS TO A SECRET PALACE EXIT...
HOLD IT RIGHT THERE!
...BUT ONE OF UNDINA'S 'LOYAL' PALACE GUARDS HAS SOLD HER OUT!

SORRY, FRIEND! YOU'RE BLOCKING TRAFFIC!
11/2

FLASH AND UNDINA ESCAPE AN AMBUSH ...AND TAKE COVER IN DENSE SEAWEED...

PLUTON'S PLANS FOR A ROYAL WEDDING HAVE HIT A SNAG...
?!
UNDINA IS GONE! AND THE EARTHLING HOSTAGES, TOO!
... THE BRIDE HAS FLOWN THE COOP.

SEARCH THE CITY! HOUSE TO HOUSE!
THEY MUST BE FOUND— ALL OF THEM!

BUT UNDINA'S CROWN JEWELS HAVE BOUGHT MORE LOYALTY THAN PLUTON'S PROMISES...
WHEN THE TRAITORS COME LOOKING, WE ATTACK!
WE ARE READY, MAJESTY!

NOW! DESTROY THEM!

THE TRAPPERS ARE TRAPPED! PLUTON'S FOLLOWERS ARE CRUSHED...

.. AND THE PALACE IS RETAKEN!
SO MUCH FOR YOUR REVOLT, PLUTON!

NOW, FLASH.. IF YOU WISH TO SEE DALE AND ZARKOV ALIVE...
...YOU WILL GIVE THIS TRAITOR A RITUAL DEATH.. IN THE DUELING ARENA!

WELL, FLASH? GET ON WITH IT!

VERY COOL, UNDINA! YOU STAGED THIS UPRISING... EVEN LED PLUTON TO BELIEVE HE COULD PULL IT OFF!
JUST TO GET *ME* DOWN HERE TO HELP!

NOW YOU WANT ME TO EXECUTE HIM... MARRY YOU... SAVE YOUR SHAKY THRONE...
...IN RETURN FOR DALE AND ZARKOV'S LIVES?
IF THAT'S HOW YOU SEE IT...

...YOU DON'T HAVE MUCH CHOICE, DO YOU, FLASH?
YOU ARE A WATER-BREATHER NOW! YOUR FUTURE IS HERE!

?!

YOU'RE WRONG, UNDINA!. THERE IS A CHOICE...

...MY FRIENDS' LIVES... OR YOURS!
NOW, WHERE ARE DALE AND ZARKOV?!
HE'S BLUFFING! SEIZE HIM!

DON'T TEST ME!
HE'S NO KILLER! DO AS I SAY!

IN AN EFFORT TO SAVE DALE AND ZARKOV'S LIVES, FLASH TAKES UNDINA HOSTAGE...
...WHILE HER GUARDS STAND BY, HELPLESS!

FLASH! LET GO! YOU'LL NEVER GET OUT OF THIS PALACE ALIVE!
THEN NEITHER WILL YOU, UNDINA!

WILL YOU TAKE ME TO DALE AND ZARKOV?
OR DO I OPEN *THIS?!*
NO! NO!! YOU'RE *MAD!*

MAD ENOUGH TO FEED *YOU* TO YOUR OWN PET EXECUTIONERS!
WELL...?
ALL RIGHT! YOU WIN!

I'LL TAKE YOU TO THEM!
THEY HAD BETTER BE UNHARMED!

THERE!
ABOARD OUR SUB?

YES, FLASH! THEY'RE BOTH PERFECTLY SAFE...
AS YOU SEE! BUT ONLY I CAN RELEASE THEM!

HARM ME... AND THEY STAY LOCKED BEHIND THIS ENERGY SCREEN...
...UNTIL THEIR AIR GIVES OUT!
YOU CAN'T WIN THIS ONE, FLASH!
11/23

OKAY, UNDINA! RELEASE THE SUB NOW... AND WE HAVE A DEAL!
YOU HAVE MY WORD!

DALE... ZARKOV! I'VE AGREED TO STAY... FOR YOUR RELEASE!
NO, FLASH! NEVER!
DON'T ARGUE! RETURN TO THE SURFACE!

FLASH IS A WATER-BREATHER NOW! WE CAN'T HELP HIM, DALE!
ZARKOV! NO! YOU CAN'T LEAVE HIM!

AND NOW, FLASH... YOU WILL ANNOUNCE YOUR DECISION TO RULE WITH ME!

WORD SPREADS THROUGH THE CORAL KINGDOM. FLASH GORDON—HERO OF THE LIBERATION—IS BACK!

AND SO, AS ALL THE KINGDOM WATCHES...
CORALIANS, WE FOUGHT TOGETHER AND WON... AGAINST THE TYRANT, MING!
YOU WERE PROMISED FREEDOM AS YOUR REWARD!

KING TRITON TRIED TO KEEP THAT PROMISE AND DIED FOR IT!
NOW YOUR QUEEN HOPES I CAN QUIET YOUR UNREST!
TRAITOR!

STOP HIM! CUT HIM OFF!
TOO LATE, UNDINA! FROM THIS THRONE, I RETURN CORALIA TO HER PEOPLE!
THE MONARCHY HAS ENDED!

FLASH'S FIRST ACT AS CO-RULER OF CORALIA IS TO RESIGN!
YOU CAN'T DO THIS!
BUT I HAVE, UNDINA!

FLASH HAS RESTORED SELF-RULE TO THE PEOPLE OF THE CORAL KINGDOM!
PUBLIC ELECTIONS WILL BE HELD.. QUEEN UNDINA AND I WILL RETIRE TO PRIVATE LIFE!

AND SO FLASH TAKES HIS LEAVE ...
PEOPLE IN POWER NEVER PAY HEAVILY FOR THEIR SINS, UNDINA!
YOU'LL RETIRE TO YOUR VILLA IN COMFORT!

MY ONLY SATISFACTION IS KNOWING YOU CANNOT RETURN TO THE SURFACE!
YOU'RE ONE OF US NOW!
DON'T BET ON THAT!

IN A SWIFT CRAFT, FLASH JETS TOWARD THE SURFACE...

BY RADIO HOOKUP, FLASH MAKES A RENDEZVOUS WITH ZARKOV...
THERE HE IS, DALE!
...WHO AWAITS HIM AT THE SURFACE!

SOON... AT THE MONGO SCIENCE CENTER...
IN A FEW HOURS HE WILL BE AN AIR-BREATHER AGAIN!
© King Features Syndicate, Inc., 1975. World rights reserved.

ZARKOV! HOW DID YOU DO IT?!
THE SAME MACHINE ONCE RESTORED US! UNDINA FORGOT WE STILL HAD IT!
12/7

THE MANKIND SERIES OF GREAT ADVENTURES OF HISTORY

GREAT MILITARY BATTLES

Library of Congress Catalog Card Number: 75-135913
SBN: 87687-009-4

Book design by Andrew Furr

CONTENTS

INTRODUCTION

Honorable men long for the time when war and tales of battles will exist only on the pages of our histories. But that time of peace has not yet come to the world. Little wars continue to sap the energy, the faith and the lifeblood of great countries. It would be interesting to read what historians of the year 2071 will write about the recent conflicts between Israel and the Arab States or America's involvement in Indochina. Certainly they will point out how these wars changed the course of the histories of the countries involved. All wars change the course of history; often it is changed by a single battle. The nine battles told about in this volume (some of which, actually, were drawn out campaigns) all changed the course of history. The span covered ranges from the American Revolution to the French defeat in Vietnam. Had Vice-Admiral Viscount Horatio Nelson failed to destroy the combined French and Spanish fleets at Trafalgar on an October afternoon in 1805 Napoleon would have realized his dream to invade Great Britain and the annals of European history would have been altered considerably. And if the Russians had not stopped the German advance at Stalingrad our histories of World War II might very well contain an account of the defeat of Russia and a negotiated ending to that war. And certainly if the French had won one crucial battle in Vietnam in 1954 the United States would never have become involved in a seemingly endless war that has drastically changed the very fabric of American life. In reading the nine tales contained in this volume one becomes painfully aware of one fact: Peace is never won through war.

RAYMOND FRIDAY LOCKE
Editor, Mankind Magazine

Lord George Grenville.

The Gaspee Affair

by Neil R. Stout

On 9 June 1772, a group of Rhode Islanders captured and burned his majesty's armed schooner *Gaspee*. This incident, and the official investigation which followed it, began a chain of events which within three years, resulted in war between Great Britain and her American colonies.

Both *Gaspee* and her commander, Lieutenant William Dudingston, were well known and vehemently hated by the American colonists, for their mission was nothing less than the enforcement of Britain's claim that the British Parliament might tax the American colonies without their consent. Great Britain emerged from the Seven Years' War (or French and Indian War, as it was called in America) in 1763 with a vastly extended empire, greatly increased responsibilities for its defense, and an unprecedented national debt. Prime

Minister George Grenville and his successors in the British government sought to shift some of the burden of the debt and imperial defense costs to Britain's thriving American colonies. Before 1763, Britain had conceded to her colonies control of their internal affairs, while the colonists, in turn, agreed to Parliament's regulation of their trade in the interests of the whole empire. Grenville changed this relationship by introducing legislation which would tax certain American imports. Americans claimed that this was "taxation without representation," that they could be taxed only by their own colonial legislatures, and that they neither had nor wanted representation in the British Parliament. Parliament nevertheless passed the Sugar Act (taxing wines and molasses imports) in 1764, the Stamp Act (taxing newspapers and legal documents) in 1765, and the Townshend Acts (taxing paper, paint, lead, glass, and tea) in 1767. The story of America's resistance to these taxes and Parliament's alleged right to levy them is the story of the American Revolution. An important chapter of that story is the *Gaspee* affair.

In 1763, as the first part of George Grenville's program for raising a revenue in the colonies, officers of the North American Squadron of the Royal Navy were sworn in as customs officers and ordered to assist the regular customs service in collecting taxes and enforcing trade regulations in America. To assist in this mission, squadron commander Rear Admiral Lord Alexander Colvill purchased six "Marblehead" sloops and schooners, which were commissioned as Royal Navy vessels, manned by navy personnel, and sent on duty as coastguard cutters. One of these little vessels was the sloop *Gaspee*, purchased at Halifax in 1764 for £420. She was forty-nine feet long and rated at seventy-seven tons. With her crew of thirty men and eight tiny guns, *Gaspee* was one of the most insignificant vessels in the Royal Navy; but she quickly made a reputation among both smugglers and honest traders as a ship to avoid. Under her first commander, Lieutenant Thomas Allen, *Gaspee* did more than any other vessel to carry out Grenville's program of naval enforcement. Early in her career the outraged seamen of Falmouth, Maine, narrowly missed destroying her; later, during the Stamp Act crisis, she helped save a shipment of hated stamps in New York.

In September, 1768, Gaspee was re-rigged as a schooner and taken over by a new commander, Lieutenant Dudingston. Her career in the waters of North America between 1768 and 1771 can be followed through angry statements in colonial newspapers. Dudlingston grew wealthy through his share from captured merchant vessels condemned in vice-admiralty court.

Sometime during the winter of 1771-72, *Gaspee* was sent to Rhode Island, the most recalcitrant of Britain's American colonies. Ever since the days of Roger Williams, Rhode Island had been an anachronism in the British empire. She had a charter which made her virtually independent, allowing her to elect all her own officials from governor on down. Almost alone among eighteenth-century communities, Rhode Island practiced democracy and religious liberty; she traded with whom she pleased—even the French during the French and Indian War—and dealt with his majesty's revenue officers in the same way she dealt with pirates. In 1764, the council of the colony signed an order to the ceremonial gunner at Fort George on Goat Island to sink *Gaspee's* sister ship, the schooner *St. John.* (The gunner, preserving a cool head, aimed his shot wide; the council reprimanded him for not carrying out orders.) Later a boat belonging to the man-of-war *Maidstone* was dragged through the streets of Newport and burned in front of the courthouse. In 1769, the revenue cutter *Liberty,* once belonging to John Hancock but used by the American Board of Customs Commissioners for their own purposes after she was condemned for smuggling, was burned in Newport Harbor by the townspeople. No one was ever brought to book for any of these incidents; nor was there ever any serious investigation made of them by Rhode Island authorities.

Lieutenant Dudingston, undeterred by the fate of his predecessors, stopped and searched everything afloat, even rowboats and market boats, and seized any that did not fulfill the letter of the law. What was worse, from the Rhode Island point of view, Dudingston ignored the Rhode Island vice-admiralty court, where Judge John Andrews could be counted upon to uphold Rhode Island interests, but instead prosecuted his seizures in the new district vice-admiralty court at Boston. When Dudingston seized and took to Boston a sloop belonging to a member of the prominent Green family, the full weight of the Rhode Island government was turned against him. Deputy Governor Darius Sessions, backed by Chief Justice Stephen Hopkins, charged that Dudingston had no valid commission as a customs officer. Governor Joseph Wanton sent the high sheriff to Dudingston with an order to present himself in person, with his commission for examination. Dudingston refused, saying he had attended the governor once, had not been asked for his commission, and he had no further business with Rhode Island's civil authorities. The lieutenant then sent copies of his correspondence with Wanton to Rear Admiral John Montagu, commander of the North American Squadron of the Royal Navy, adding that plans were afoot to destroy *Gaspee* and arrest him.

The exchange between Wanton and Montagu which followed must surely be among the most acrimonious that ever took place between two public officials. Montagu said he was ashamed to find such letters coming from one of his majesty's governors, that if the people of Rhode Island made any attempt against *Gaspee*, "I will hang them as pirates," and "I would advise you not to send your sheriff on board the king's ship again, on such ridiculous errands." Wanton replied that "I do not receive instructions for the administration of my government from the King's admiral . . . I will send the sheriff of this colony at any time, and to any place, within the body of it, as I shall think fit." Montagu sent a complaint about Wanton to the admiralty, while Wanton sent his charges against Montagu to the colonial secretary. The admiral also ordered the man-of-war *Beaver* to Rhode Island to protect *Gaspee* and to make the Rhode Islanders "behave in the future with more respect to the King's officers."

On 9 June 1772, *Gaspee* attempted to stop the packet boat *Hannah* on her regular run from Newport to Providence. The packet refused to heave to and led *Gaspee* into shoal water where she grounded off Namquit Point, about seven miles below Providence. An anonymous informer, possibly Customs Collector Charles Dudley, claimed that the grounding was part of a carefully laid plot. After failing to entice Dudingston ashore, the Rhode Islanders allegedly picked Captain Benjamin Lindsey of *Hannah*, because he knew the waters of Narragansett Bay well, to lure *Gaspee* aground. Whether it was deliberate or not, the schooner was grounded, and Lindsey hastened to Providence to report her predicament. She could not be refloated until after midnight. That was what the Rhode Islanders had been waiting for. A drummer spread the news along the main street, and by ten o'clock several boatloads of armed men were ready. Rowing with muffled oars, they got to within sixty yards of the schooner before being challenged.

Abraham Whipple, captain of a West Indiaman and later commodore in the American Navy, answered: "I am the sheriff of the county of Kent, G-d d--n you. I

The Burning of the Gaspee.

have got a warrant to apprehend you, G-d d--n you; so surrender, G-d d--n you." Dudingston ordered the boats to keep off, but was immediately felled by musket wounds in his arm and groin. His badly outnumbered crew quickly gave up. The lieutenant's wounds were tended by his captors and he was put ashore, where he was arrested almost at once on a heavy damage suit brought by Thomas Green. *Gaspee* herself was put to the torch and burned to the waterline by daylight.

As soon as he heard of the affair, Admiral Montagu began gathering statements from Dudingston and his crew. These he sent to the admiralty in London along with the observation that "the inhabitants of Rhode Island in general are a set of Lawless Piratical people, whose whole business is that of Smuggling." Joseph Wanton, said Montagu, was a fit governor for such a people. The admiral sent five men-of-war to the tiny colony. One of them was *Mercury*, commanded by Captain Robert Keeler. While on station, Keeler seized and successfully prosecuted a brig carrying contraband rum and sugar; but during the auction of the cargo, a mob liberated the condemned items. When Keeler came ashore to see about it, he was served with four writs of arrest, one from the owner of the brig for robbery, two from her master and crew for unlawfully detaining them, and one from the government of Rhode Island for kidnapping. Keeler noted to Montagu that serving in Rhode Island "requires great patience." The British Treasury paid for his defense.

In July 1772, the first break came in the *Gaspee* case. Captain John Linzee of H.M.S. *Beaver* captured a runaway slave named Aaron. Aaron, allegedly after being threatened with torture by Captain Linzee, confessed that he was one of the men who burned *Gaspee* and named five prominent citizens of Providence and Bristol as participants. Montagu at once sent copies of

Aaron's statement to England and ordered Linzee not to let the slave out of his custody. Almost as soon as he received word of Aaron's confession, Governor Wanton took three statements that proved, if they were legitimate, that Aaron had been in bed between two other slaves the whole night of the *Gaspee* affair. Wanton sent the sheriff of Newport County to *Beaver* with a warrant for Aaron's arrest, but Linzee refused to give the slave up. Soon after, Aaron's master had Linzee arrested for stealing the slave, and Admiral Montagu had to bail his captain out of jail. After that, the admiral told Governor Wanton, he was doubly sure he would never allow the navy's star witness to fall into Rhode Island hands.

Acting on the information sent by Montagu, King George III ordered a royal commission to inquire into the destruction of *Gaspee*. The commission was to be composed of some of the most distinguished jurists in the colonies: Chief Justices Frederick Smythe of New Jersey, Daniel Horsmanden of New York, and Peter Oliver of Massachusetts, Judge Robert Auchmuty of the Boston district vice-admiralty court, and Governor Joseph Wanton. The commission was empowered to subpoena and examine under oath any persons it chose. If it discovered any of the offenders, the commission was to turn them over to the civil authorities of Rhode Island, "that they may be accordingly arrested and delivered to the custody of the commander-in-chief of our ships and vessels in North America," to be taken to England for trial. The commissioners were also empowered to apply to General Thomas Gage for army protection if they thought it was necessary.

The powers of the *Gaspee* Commission were about the same as those of a committee of the United States Congress: it had almost limitless authority to investigate, but arrests and indictments were still the prerogative of the local law enforcement agencies and courts.

Americans, however, partly from ignorance of what the commission's instructions from the king really said, and partly because it was a heaven-sent propaganda opportunity, spread the word that the commission had much broader powers. It was supposed to be able to arrest citizens for any reason or none, using the army and navy if need be, to turn them over directly to Admiral Montagu for transportation to England. The *Providence Gazette* called it "a Court of Inquisition, more horrid than that of Spain." Most Americans seemed to agree. Even though their fears were based on false assumptions, they were not unimportant. Fear of the *Gaspee* commission led the Virginia House of Burgesses to propose, in March 1773, that permanent intercolonial committees of correspondence be set up. Other colonies gladly adopted the proposal. The committees of correspondence, as the Reverend Ezra Stiles predicted in 1773, led to the creation of a Continental Congress. Thus the *Gaspee* affair became a prime mover of American independence.

As for the feared *Gaspee* commission in action, only an operetta by Gilbert and Sullivan could do justice to it. Its august members with their Gilbertian names assembled at Newport (where the British government mistakenly thought the *Gaspee* outrage had occurred) on 5 January 1773, and received their instructions and commissions from Captain Keeler, acting for Admiral Montagu. (Montagu had to ask for a safe conduct for Keeler, as the captain was still being arrested every time he stepped ashore in Rhode Island.) The first business the commissioners transacted, even before taking their oaths, was to send a demand that Admiral Montagu himself come to Newport to be ready to receive any prisoners. Montagu answered that his instructions allowed him to appoint a captain to receive prisoners, that the king's business required his presence at naval headquarters in Boston, and that his flagship, *Captain*, could not go to sea in the middle of winter. Nevertheless, he said he would come to Newport unless the commissioners let him off.

The admiral set off overland from Boston to the Taunton River, an arm of Narragansett Bay, where Montagu boarded the frigate *Lizard* and sailed into Newport Harbor in the style that befitted his station, his blue admiral's flag flying proudly from *Lizard's* main topmast. The battery on Goat Island greeted him with perfect silence. Enraged, Montagu sent Captain Inglis of *Lizard* ashore to demand an explanation of the affront from Governor Wanton. Wanton blandly told Inglis that Rhode Island's budget provided for salutes to be fired only on certain holidays, such as the king's birthday. Montagu's complaint got all the way to King George III, who was "justly incensed" and ordered that "His Majesty's ships of war, coming into any of the ports within the colony of Rhode Island, and having an admiral's flag or broad pennant hoisted, be saluted in such manner as is usual in all other parts of His Majesty's dominions in America."

On 16 January, three days after he arrived in Newport, Montagu informed the commissioners that he was leaving, "until I can come in a proper manner, and a proper season of the year." The commissioners testily replied that they were "not utter strangers" to the fact that the weather was bad, but they stuck to their own interpretation of their instructions. They sent a complaint about Montagu's departure to the colonial secretary and then adjourned until May. By the time the commission met again, London had ruled that Montagu could delegate his business with it to Captain Keeler. The admiral gladly canceled his trip to Rhode Island for, as he told Lord Sandwich, "I am clear nothing will ever come of that Commission."

No one was arrested as a result of the *Gaspee* Commission's investigations. If anyone was indicted, it was

The Boston Tea Party.

the Royal Navy itself. The commissioners criticized Captain Linzee for not turning Aaron over to the sheriff of Newport County when a proper warrant was presented for his arrest, and for treating "the civil authority in a most contemptuous and unjustifiable manner." The commission further charged "that the conduct of Captain Linzee tended too strongly to extort from a weak or wicked mind declarations not strictly true." With that the commission threw out the testimony of the navy's star witness, the slave Aaron. Lieutenant Dudingston was accused of imprudence in refusing to show his commission to Governor Wanton. "There is also too much reason to believe," noted the commissioners, "that in some instances Lieutenant Dudingston from an intemperate, if not reprehensible zeal to aid the revenue service, exceeded the bounds of his duty." All the commissioners, even Joseph Wanton, remained loyal to the king during the Revolution, and all except Wanton were supporters of Parliament's authority over the colonies; but they proved beyond all doubt that they were not "tools of the ministry," as propagandists had charged.

It was half a century before anyone admitted having a part in burning *Gaspee*. Lieutenant Dudingston recovered from his wounds and returned to England to be tried by court-martial for loss of his ship. His acquittal was a formality, the main controversy coming over whether the navy or the customs service should reimburse him for his losses. He was granted a pension, promoted to captain, and sent to a French spa to complete recovery from his wounds. Commissioner Daniel Horsmanden filed a separate report with the colonial secretary, Lord Dartmouth, in which he complained that Rhode Island's "Government (if it deserves that name) is a downright democracy." Horsmanden urged that Rhode Island and Connecticut be combined into a single colony and placed under a royal governor; but others had made that suggestion, and no more was heard from Horsmanden.

Thus ended the *Gaspee* affair, so far as official Britain was concerned. But it had set in motion a chain of events that led, within two years after the commission finished its deliberations, to open war between the American colonies and the mother country and ultimately to American independence. Americans, frightened by the precedent of a special royal commission operating outside their own legal system, kept in being the committees of correspondence set up to combat the *Gaspee* Commission. They had not long to wait for a new issue. While the commission met, the British Parliament passed the famous Tea Act which gave a monopoly of tea sales in America to the East India Company, cut the price of tea to American consumers below that "honestly smuggled" from Holland but retained the 1767 tax on tea which was to be collected in American ports for revenue purposes. The committees of correspondence quickly spread the word that Britain was using cheap tea to seduce Americans into paying an unconstitutional tax. They called popular meetings which resolved that not a pound of taxable tea should be landed in America, and such groups as Sam Adams' Boston "Mohawks" and Philadelphia's "Committee for Tarring and Feathering" prepared to enforce the resolutions.

Fate and the sea determined that the first tea ships should arrive at Boston, the center of revolutionary activity for over a decade. Boston's "Tea Party" came first and she was the target of the punitive Intolerable Acts passed by Parliament; but many other colonial port cities had their own "Tea Parties" during the first months of 1774. When Boston's punishment became known, the committees of correspondence throughout the colonies came to her aid, and through them came the call for a Continental Congress to decide upon a united American stand against the British measures. The government of the United States of America dates from the first meeting of the Continental Congress in September, 1774. Its origins can be traced to the *Gaspee* affair; for the committees of correspondence first set up as propaganda agencies to fight the *Gaspee* Commission, were responsible for calling the First Continental Congress. Thus the misplaced zeal of a Royal Navy lieutenant and some Rhode Island hotheads ironically had a constructive end.

Lexington and Concord, Bunker Hill, and the War for American Independence pushed Rhode Island and the *Gaspee* affair into the background, but the Royal Navy remembered its humiliation and sought revenge. During the war, Captain James Wallace of H.M.S. *Rose*, with his squadron, shelled Bristol, looted the lower part of Narragansett Bay, and practically starved Newport. But Rhode Islanders and Commodore Abraham Whipple's descendants in southern Ohio still savor the last word by telling of this exchange of terse notes:

You, Abraham Whipple, on the 10th June 1772, burned his Majesty's vessel, the *Gaspee*, and I will hang you at the yard arm. (signed) James Wallace.

To Sir James Wallace; Sir: Always catch a man before you hang him. (signed) Abraham Whipple.

Trafalgar: The Last Battle

by George Stephens Clark

*T*he retreat across a thousand miles of hostile Russian steppes may have been the funeral march for the Grand Army, but it was his inability to cross some thirty miles of water that eventually doomed the schemes of Napoleon Bonaparte. If l'Empereur had ever been able to cross the English Channel and defeat his most persistent enemy, it goes without saying that the entire course of world history would have been greatly altered. But Great Britain was never invaded, and the credit for this must be given to one remarkable man: Vice-Admiral Viscount Horatio Nelson.

To have made the invasion the French would have had to gain control of the channel long enough to transport the troops across, but on a bloodfilled October afternoon off the coast of southern Spain, Lord

Nelson ended all French hopes for an invasion when he met and effectively destroyed the combined French and Spanish fleets. This battle, known now as Trafalgar, was the final victory for Nelson and the British navy. The admiral and four hundred and fifty English seamen were killed. But never again was the French Empire able to muster a significant threat on the high seas.

In 1803 at the end of the year of peace after the Treaty of Amiens, hostilities between France and England were renewed and Napoleon's army was still encamped on the shores of the English Channel. Again the threat of an invasion hung over the British Isles.

The blockade of French ports which Nelson had helped organize in 1801 was set up again. In the channel and along the northern coasts Admiral William Cornwallis maintained the British watch. That close to home, the English strategy was to keep the blockade so tight that the French ships could never move from their ports. This was the most logical and reasonable defense and with the capable Cornwallis in command it worked successfully. In all weather and around the clock for over two years the British ships stayed on the French horizon. During that entire period the French squadron at Brest made only one half-hearted attempt to escape, but at the first sign of the approaching Englishmen they turned and sailed back to port.

But in the south, along the coast of Spain (which shortly entered the war as an ally of France) and in the Mediterranean, the English naval strategy was different. The same blockade was maintained, but it was with the constant hope that the enemy would someday come out and fight a decisive battle in which they would be destroyed.

Bonaparte himself was one of the British navy's greatest assets because he never gained an understanding of naval warfare and throughout his career he continued to think of his navy as an army on water. Ships which could sail onward day and night, while an army on the move was required to stop and camp, could cover a thousand miles in half the time of a galloping horseman. But these ships, depending upon winds, currents, and shore lines, might take several days to maneuver into position for battle while a unit of cavalry might execute the same tactical move in less than half an hour. Napoleon's landlocked genius never grasped this reality. He felt that if he could bring together enough ships then they could march (sail) forward to their goal sweeping away any smaller force in their way. This was the misconception behind Napoleon's plan for all the French and Spanish squadrons to break out of the blockade, rendezvous in the West Indies, and then to sail into the channel as one vast armada and hold control until the invasion could be made.

Nelson hoped that Napoleon would grow impatient and try to force his navy into action, so as he kept the blockade at Toulon he hid his main strength out at sea and watched the port with a small squadron of picket ships. He wanted the enemy to come out so that he could engage them in battle, thus he offered them every opportunity. And they did come out. The young and tragic French Admiral Villeneuve twice managed to bring his fleet past Nelson. The first time the French were forced back to port by foul weather. The second escape became the first in a series of events which found their climax at Trafalgar.

When Villeneuve slipped out of Toulon the first time, Nelson made a calculated guess that the French were headed for Egypt. He was in error and only the favorable intervention of nature kept his mistake from being a fatal one. When the French managed to get away the second time, Nelson was not so quick to

G. Chambers' painting, "The Battle of Trafalgar."
(Maritime Museum, London)

jump. He waited off Sardinia until he had positive information about the destination of his enemy. After ten days word came that Villeneuve had passed through the Straits of Gibraltar and was in the Atlantic.

Villeneuve, joined by the Spanish ships at Cadiz, carried out his orders and sailed to the West Indies to await the units of the French Atlantic squadrons. But Brest remained closed under the tight surveillance of Cornwallis, and the ships that were to join Villeneuve were never able to leave port. As he waited, Villeneuve received news that Nelson's fleet had followed him and that they had arrived in the area. He waited no longer. Instead of taking the chance of being forced into a battle that he was neither prepared nor capable of fighting, Villeneuve raced back across the Atlantic for the safety of a friendly port.

So for a second time, Nelson had failed to locate and destroy the French. Feeling that he had lost the opportunity he most sought, Nelson sailed back to Gibraltar to begin once more the tedious blockade duty. He was disappointed and tired of the endless months at sea, so he took the leave due him and returned to England. For twenty-five days the admiral relaxed in the peace of his country estate at Merton before returning to the sea to win his final victory.

While Nelson rested, Villeneuve searched for a better port and shifted his fleet south to Cadiz which was blockaded by Admiral Collingwood. The English squadron was too small, however, to offer any resistance, so they stood back and allowed the French and Spanish ships to enter the harbor. Immediately Collingwood dispatched Captain Blackwood (the best of the frigate captains) on the *Euryalus* (the fastest of the frigates) to take the news to England that Villeneuve was at Cadiz.

Blackwood landed in Portsmouth on September 2, and left at once to carry the message, first to Nelson at

Nelson at Trafalgar.

Merton, and then on to London. Villeneuve had been found and Nelson would have yet another chance to draw the enemy into action. "Depend upon it, Blackwood," Nelson said, "I shall yet give Monsieur Villeneuve a beating." Ten days later the *Victory* was underway sailing south with the admiral's flag hoisted.

Nelson was filled with renewed enthusiasm, for in the quiet of the English country side he had finished working out his plan for battle. The tactical concepts of the plan were without precedent. An entirely new style of naval battle would be fought, and the boldness of the plan, as well as the manner in which it was finally executed, stand as testimonials to the genius of Nelson as much as the resulting victory itself.

He discussed his plan openly while in England. He explained and elaborated to Lady Hamilton, to fellow naval officers, to politicians, and to social friends. And each time he discussed it, he would see it more clearly.

Captain Keats of the *Superb* visited one afternoon and as he and Nelson walked through the gardens the admiral explained the plan. Keats recorded Nelson's words. "No day can be long enough to arrange a couple of fleets and fight a decisive battle, according to the old system." This "old system" was to place the fleet in a single line parallel to the enemy's line and then shoot it out. If a ship could be brought across its opponent's bow or stern where the enemy could not bring their guns to bear, then so much the better. This maneuver, however, was more characteristic of individual combat rather than fleet contests.

"I shall form the fleet into three divisions in three lines," Nelson told Keats. "One division shall be composed of twelve or fourteen of the fastest two-decked ships, which I shall always keep to windward, or in a situation of advantage; and I shall put them under an officer who, I am sure, will employ them in the manner I wish, if possible.

"I consider it will always be in my power to throw them into battle in any part I may choose; but if circumstances prevent their being carried against the enemy where I desire, I shall feel certain he will employ them effectively, and perhaps in a more advantageous manner than if he could have followed my orders.

"With the remaining part of the fleet formed in two lines, I shall go at them at once, if I can, about one third of their line from the leading ship . . . I think it will surprise and confound the enemy. They won't know what I am about. It will bring forward a pell mell battle, and that is what I want."

But Nelson failed to mention the one major factor that would make such a "pell mell" battle be to his advantage. He failed to mention it perhaps, because it was something that was just understood and unnecessary to state. This was the absolute conviction that the superior seamanship, gunnery, and morale of the English sailor would guarantee victory once the ships were joined. And this was not just the attitude of a proud admiral, but a fact and a reality; the English seamen were indeed far superior.

But what makes sailors of one navy more skillfull than those of another? A single storm drove the French back to Toulon, but the English ships continued to stand off shore in all manner of weather for over two years. On his dash to the West Indies and back Villeneuve returned with over a thousand sick men and few of his ships were in any shape to do battle by the time they reached Cadiz. Nelson's fleet made the same trip and returned still seeking a confrontation with the enemy. While there are probably many subtle influences (such as the Englishman's nautical heritage) there are two major causes which help explain this difference between the two navies.

The first reason for English superiority was leadership. Trust and respect generally typified the attitude of the British seaman towards his officers, while in the French and Spanish fleets the officers did not even trust each other. Nelson received a devotion from his officers and crews that was nothing short of love; below decks on the French ships rumors were whispered that Villeneuve was a coward who would never fight. Ship's captains in the English navy eagerly accepted invitations to the flagship just to enjoy their commander's company, but when Villeneuve attempted a staff meeting tempers flared so violently between the French and Spanish officers that swords were drawn and threats made.

Each of these attitudes at the command level filtered down through the respective fleets until the individual ships' crews reflected them. On one side there was a trust that produced high morale, pride, and confidence. The other side felt only a defeating hopelessness.

The second valid cause for this difference of ability was the fact that the British navy was at sea and the French and Spanish fleets were in port. Here again Napoleon showed his ignorance of naval affairs. He believed that the long blockade would wear the English down while his sailors rested and conserved themselves on shore. Just the opposite was true. As a company of cavalry would hardly be elite if they only mounted their horses on the day of a battle, or a regiment of infantry could never effectively maneuver if they failed to drill, the same is true of sailors. During the years of blockade duty the English seamen trained and practiced their drills until they reached a state of super efficiency. The French and Spanish crews could not even learn to gain their sea legs as long as they never went to sea.

So these factors led to the development of the opposing navies one that was skilled, efficient, and confident, and another that could barely sail, much less fight and

Lady Hamilton.
(Maritime Museum, London)

win a battle. These were the pending contenders when on September 28, 1805 the *Victory* rejoined the fleet which had gathered before Cadiz. Admiral Collingwood, who was now second in command, summed up the reaction of the fleet when he wrote to his wife, "Lord Nelson is arrived . . . a sort of general joy has been the consequence."

Nelson wasted no time in calling his captains to the flagship. Probably they would not have questioned their admiral's judgment no matter what plan he offered, but there was an immediate and genuine excitement when he laid out his strategy. In a letter to Lady Hamilton, Nelson said, ". . . and when I came to explain the 'Nelson touch' (his pet name for the plan) it was like an electric shock. Some shed tears, all approved. 'It was new—it was singular—it was simple!,' and from admirals downwards, it was repeated: 'It must succeed, if ever they will allow us to get at them!' "

To "get at them" Nelson again pulled his main fleet out of sight and kept watch on the port through a line of frigates. The fleet stayed well out to sea and to the southwest of Cadiz where they were far enough away not to scare the enemy back to port, but not so far as to allow them time to escape again. On October 19, 1805 a signal came from the *Euryalus* that the enemy was beginning to move.

It was too late in the year to attempt a massive crossing of the stormy channel, so Napoleon, at least for a while, decided to abandon the invasion. There were still lands that could be conquered on the continent without the help of his navy. Besides, he felt that his admiral's failure to carry out his orders was because of their incompetence rather than the impossibility of his plans, and so he no longer trusted them to execute anything critical to his future operations. The next set of orders to Villeneuve were for him to move from

Lord Cuthbert Collingwood.
(Maritime Museum, London)

Cadiz to the Mediterranean where he would transport troops rather than be depended upon to fight.

It was a degrading assignment for the combined fleet, but it was at least one they could hope to accomplish. Villeneuve already feared that the emperor had lost confidence in him and rather than feeling disappointed by the insignificance of this new assignment, he was elated at having a second chance. Actually Napoleon was not intending to give him one. Already the emperor had decided to replace Villeneuve, but by the time word reached Cadiz, the admiral had sailed.

Villeneuve knew his fleet was not yet in condition for serious action, but he was anxious to get started and decided to take the first opportunity. Then on the night of October 18, the winds shifted and came from the northeast; favorable for a dash to Gibraltar. At dawn Villeneuve gave orders to sail, and almost at once the breeze began to fail. All day the fleet worked to get out of port, but it was Sunday morning, the 20th, before the last ship had cleared the harbor and the fleet got underway. By that time, Nelson had already begun to move to intercept him.

When the first French ships began to make sail on the 19th, they were watched by the *Sirius* and she reported the activity to the *Euryalus,* the next ship in the long line that stretched forty-eight miles to the main English fleet. By 7 a.m. it was obvious that the French and Spanish were getting underway and the *Sirius* hoisted the signal "370." In the new English signal code book under the three numbers "370" it read, "Enemy ships are coming out of port." In quick succession the message was transfered from the *Sirius* to the *Euryalus,* to the *Phoebe,* to the *Naiad,* to the *Defence,* to the *Colossus,* to the *Mars,* to the *Victory.* By 9:30 a.m., almost 24 hours before the last French ship began to move, Nelson knew his adversary was coming out. The English admiral made his first order to the fleet, "general chase," and set a course southeast toward Gibraltar.

The line of signal frigates continued to stalk the enemy all that day and through the night. As Villeneuve struggled to get out of the harbor and Nelson shifted his main body southward, English seamanship was already paying off. Nelson knew every move his opponent made while Villeneuve floundered along trying to guess where and when the attack might come.

By the morning of the 20th, Nelson could see the Straits of Gibraltar and the French were not yet in sight. Nothing remained for the English but to wait patiently as Villeneuve blindly continued to sail straight into their hands.

As the sun rose the next morning the waking men of the English fleet began to swarm on deck, for on the eastern horizon, off the Cape of Trafalgar, the sails of the enemy were coming into view. Nelson was in high spirits. It was October 21, the same date that his uncle had fought and won a sea battle against the French forty-eight years before. Excitement began to spread among the English crews; at long last they were going to fight. Ten minutes later, at 6 a.m., the morning light had crawled far enough to the west for the French and Spanish to see their waiting foe.

Nelson sent Hardy, the *Victory's* captain, to order the hoisting of the first signal, "Form the order of sailing." This was more formality than necessity, for with the exception of the *Africa* (which had become separated from the fleet during the night) the ships of the English fleet were already in their proper places. At 6:20 a.m., approximately ten minutes later, Villeneuve hoisted his first order: "Form a line of battle in normal sequence." This was basically the same order Nelson had given, but the thirty-three ships of the French were still in such disorder from coming out of port, that it would have taken most of a day for them to reach their proper stations.

Seamanship was the difference. The English were exhibiting the efficiency that they would continue to maintain throughout the day, and the French and Spanish vainly struggled to resolve the chaos that would epitomize their condition during the entire battle.

The direction of the wind was to the British advantage, but it blew so softly that it was seldom more than a breeze. The elements, which would rage so fiercely in a storm two days later, were passive and calm before the pending man-made violence. The wind was so light that when the guns began firing the smoke hung above them and did not blow away. (Nelson had foreseen this possible problem, and had all of his ships paint their masts with yellow stripes so that they could be identified above the smoke.) During the battle the weakness of the wind was such that to the men of both sides it would seem an eternity before a ship could come about or execute a maneuver. The fleets were about ten miles apart when they had first seen each other, but it took the fastest English ships six hours to close the distance.

Nelson signaled his fleet to prepare for battle, then followed that with the order, "Bear up in succession on the course set by the Admiral," and he swung on to an east by northeast course. A short time later he made his last maneuver and set the course due east. After that there was nothing but the waiting as the dragging hours passed and the fleets drew slowly together.

For two hours after the British had first been sighted Villeneuve debated whether to try and reach the Straits or to turn back to Cadiz. His advance ships were far enough along to reach Gibraltar before the English caught them, but the center and rear of his line would have to fight their way through. On the other hand, if he turned back most of his ships should stand a good chance of making it even though it would mean aban-

Thomas Masterman Hardy.
(Maritime Museum, London)

doning those units now out in front. But one other factor was probably the cause of his final decision: if an engagement could not be avoided, then Villeneuve wanted to be near enough to a friendly port for any damaged ships to be able to reach it. Around 8 a.m. he hoisted the order to turn and form the line of battle in reverse order.

Tactically, Villeneuve's decision was correct. If he had been commanding an English squadron they probably could have made the turn and reached port without serious losses. But Villeneuve was commanding a fleet of ships that were in poor condition, manned by untrained crews, and in a state of complete disorder. The maneuver to turn was a disaster and even though he was able to get the majority into proper order before the shooting began, they were so scattered and irregularly spaced that they were never able to form an effective battle line.

About seven o'clock that morning the English ships formed into two lines, one behind Nelson on the *Victory* and the other behind Collingwood on the *Royal Sovereign.* This was slightly different from Nelson's original plan of three lines, and it was only the first of several changes the Admiral would make; changes as controversial and unprecedented as the initial concept.

It was probably his direction of approach that later drew the most criticism, for Nelson attacked directly on a line perpendicular to the enemy's line rather than closing for action on an angle. The guns of a sailing ship fired to the sides and not forward or to the stern, and the English were sailing directly into the French guns without being able to bring their own weapons to bear. This meant that the lead ships of Nelson's two divisions "would be under effective fire from four or five enemy ships, perhaps 200 guns, for the last thousand yards of their approach. As the breeze lay, it would take them at least twenty minutes to cover that distance, and in twenty minutes some thousands of shots might be fired at each of them."

In other words, rather than crossing the "T" to bring his broadsides to bear on the enemy's point, he was trying to break through the middle of the French line and in doing so he deliberately allowed the enemy line to become the crossbar of a "T" formation. His hope was to divide the larger force so that the rear and vanguard could not position to support each other, but in doing so he was taking the chance that his ships might be sunk or stopped before they could even return fire.

This is a valid criticism except for some very important considerations. First, Nelson knew that because of the blockade the French and Spanish gunners had not had any practice in over two years. Also, since the enemy was sailing almost directly across the wind, they would have to fire from heavily rolling ships. And this was more than an inconvenience to the enemy. The French used the older "slow match" to fire their guns instead of a spark from a flint-lock, so rather than being able to shoot as the rolling gun came on target, their gunners had to estimate the roll and the burning time of the fuse, and just hope that it ignited at the right instant.

Nelson also took under consideration the fact that the French gunners were instructed to aim high, for the masts, rather than for the hull as the English gunners did. The English method reflected their self-confidence in that they expected to capture the ship and it would be worth more as a prize if the rigging was still intact. Also, if the English aim was too low the ball would tend to skim off the water and still inflict some damage. If the shot was high, it might still effectively damage the sails and masts.

The French method showed a defensive attitude, for to shoot away a foe's sails simply prevented him from pursuing. A ship without sails could not move, but as

Cartoon satirizing Napoleon's hopes of invading Great Britain by sea.

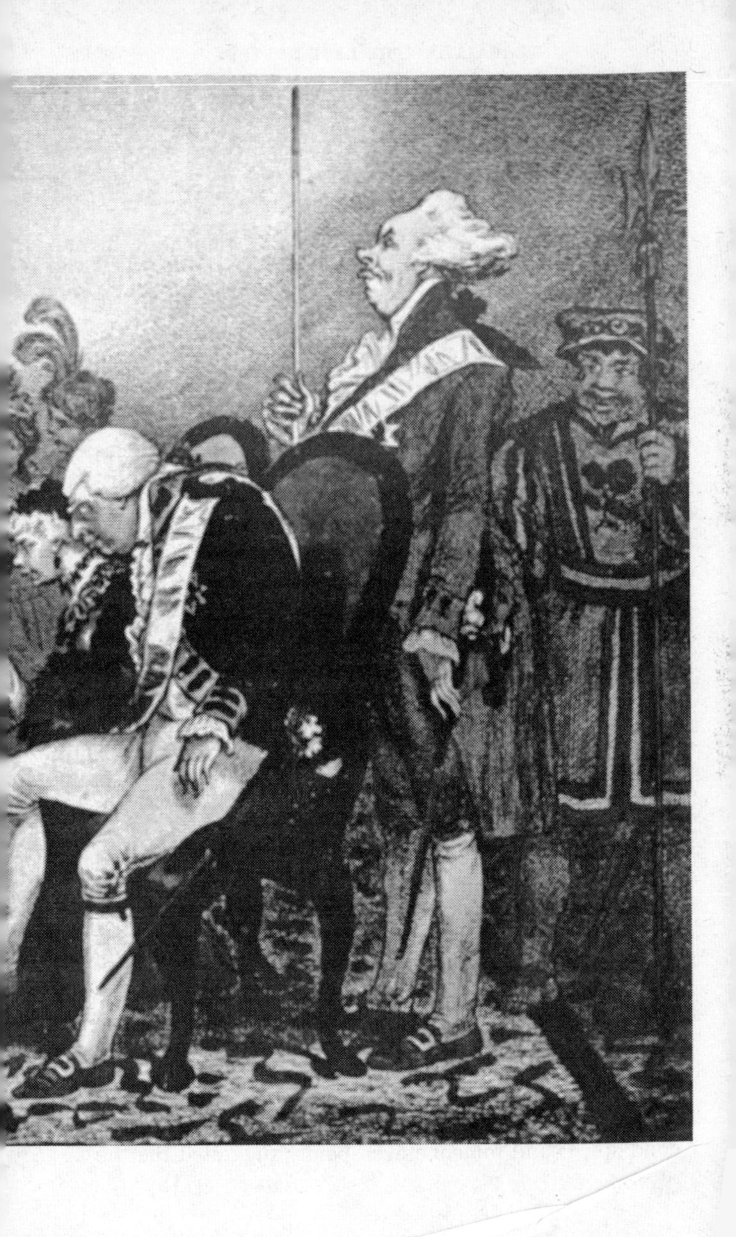

long as its guns were not damaged, it could still fight. Also, when the French aim was high, the shot went over, hitting nothing, and because chain shot instead of ball was used against rigging, a low hit did less damage.

But the admiral was probably most influenced toward his decision to attack straight on by the fact that if he took time to maneuver, the enemy would be allowed enough time to escape again. He considered the actual significance of the risks involved and judged them worth taking in light of the opportunity that was offered.

Nelson made his decisions and then stood with his staff on the poop deck of the *Victory* watching the distance between the fleets slowly close as the sun inched higher in the sky. At nine o'clock, five miles to go. Eleven o'clock: three miles. Collingwood's line had drawn a little ahead and would contact the enemy first. Eagerness, tension, impatience mounted with the dragging minutes. This was to be the fight for which they had all waited so long.

The tension grew in Nelson, too, and he began to pace. It was going as he had planned. It would work. The enemy ships were close enough to recognize now. Once more he ran all the factors through his mind, for he had waited so long for this and there could be no mistake. He wondered if anything had been left undone. Perhaps some final word to the men would be in order. The admiral turned to Blackwood, who had come aboard from the *Euryalus* earlier that morning, and asked if there was "not yet one [a signal] wanting." The frigate captain replied that everyone seemed to understand what to do. "Suppose," said Nelson, "we telegraph 'Nelson confides that every man will do his duty'."

Those around the English commander agreed in good spirits and someone even boldly suggested that he substitute "England" for "Nelson." The Admiral liked the idea and made the change. "Mr. Pasco," he said to his flag lieutenant, "I wish to say to the fleet, 'England confides that every man will do his duty.' You must be quick, for I have one more to make, which is close for action."

The flag lieutenant pointed out that it would be quicker if he used "expects" instead of "confides." The second would have to be spelled out with the flags, while the first was in the code book and could be made faster. Nelson nodded his agreement and said, "That will do, Pasco, make it directly."

It was 11:35 a.m. as the flags rose to the *Victory's* yardarms and one of history's most inspiring and remembered quotations flashed to the fleet. *England expects that every man will do his duty.* It flew there briefly, just long enough to be read, and then it was lowered as another signal went up: "Engage the enemy more closely."

"Now I can do no more," Nelson said. "We must trust to the great disposer of all events, and to the justice of our cause." The commander-in-chief's job was done. He had found and caught his enemy and brought the English ships into action at the place and in the manner he most believed would result in victory. He expected to capture at least twenty of the enemy's ships, for there was no doubt in Nelson's mind that there would be anything except a total British victory.

Collingwood's line would be in action at any moment as he steered for the sixteenth ship from the rear of the French line. He was taking on more opponents than he had been told, but he had recognized the *Santa Ana,* the huge flagship of Spanish Vice-Admiral de Alava. It was a worthy prize to pursue.

It was ten minutes to noon when the guns of the French *Fougueux* roared the opening shots. Collingwood fired a round, but it was only to create a smoke

The deck of the Victory *when Nelson fell.*
(Maritime Museum, London)

The death of Nelson.
(Maritime Museum, London)

screen. The *Royal Sovereign* was out in front of the rest of the line and the whole fleet watched as Collingwood sailed straight towards the flashing guns of more than half a dozen foes. He was defenseless, unable to return fire and like all of the first ships to drive for the French line, he suffered heavy damage.

The *Victory* would lose twenty men (including Mr. Scott, Nelson's secretary) and have thirty wounded before it could even fire a shot. The French fire was hurting the English, but it could not stop them. On board the *Belleisle,* the second ship in Collingwood's division, the deck was littered with dead. One of the officers suggested to the captain that they turn parallel and return fire. "No," the captain answered, "We are ordered to go through the line, and go through she shall, by God!"

And go through they did. First the *Royal Sovereign* when she slipped between the French *Fougueux* and the Spanish *Santa Ana.* It was now the turn of the English gunners and in less than the sixty seconds it took to go past the *Santa Ana* they fired 125 rounds into the unprotected stern from a range of less than thirty yards.

As the *Victory* aimed to cut between the French ships *Redoutable* and *Bucentaure,* the *Redoutable* came up close so that there was no room to sail between them. Captain Hardy pointed out to Nelson that it was impossible to get through without going on board one of the French ships. "I cannot help that," Nelson answered. "But it does not signify which one we run on board of. Go aboard which you please. Take your choice." Hardy chose the *Redoutable* and rammed into its bow and locked up.

Within minutes the rest of the English ships began to select their victims and cut into the line. The "pell mell" battle was underway with dozens of individual fights taking place. Smoke filled the air and isolated both friends and foes. Each ship felt as if it were fighting alone, but in an area no more than half a mile wide and a little over a mile long there were sixty warships joined in battle. For approximately four hours the battle raged as death and smoke and glory and terror filled the air.

Then the superior skill of the English began to tell. They were outsailing, out-fighting, and out-gunning their enemy. They had cut the French line into three parts and by 2:15 p.m. the enemy ships of the center, the *Bucentaure*, *Redoutable*, *Fougueux*, and *Santisima Trinidad* were all out of action. Within another fifteen minutes it was clear that a British victory was certain in the rear section. Already six of the French had surrendered and those still resisting were attempting to escape. The action in the lead section took longer, but the result was the same and around 4:15 p.m. the signal was made from the *Victory* to "Come to the wind on the starboard tack," which meant to cease pursuit and regroup. The battle was over.

Many of the British ships were damaged extensively and would be lost in the storm that rose during the following days, but none of the English ships had struck colors. Most of the French and Spanish ships were destroyed, captured or disabled beyond repair, and Admiral Villeneuve himself had been captured. It had been a total victory for Nelson's fleet, but a victory accompanied by tragedy.

Horatio Nelson had only witnessed about twenty minutes of the battle before a musket ball struck him. The shot came from the rigging of the enemy ship alongside and it slammed down through the admiral's shoulder and into his chest. "They have done for me at last, Hardy," he cried, and when Hardy said no, Nelson replied, "Oh yes, my backbone is shot through."

He was carried to the surgeon, Dr. Beatty, but Nelson had been right; there was no hope for him. He lay dying all through the battle, sometimes asking about the action, sometimes talking of death, sometimes speaking incoherently. Around four o'clock Captain Hardy went below to see Nelson and to congratulate him on a complete victory. The news seemed to please him.

Then during the next half an hour Nelson began to fail. His voice was very faint and those still with him knelt beside him to hear his words. "Doctor," he said, speaking to Dr. Scott, the chaplain, "I have not been a great sinner." The admiral paused to gain his breath. "Remember that I leave Lady Hamilton and my daughter Horatia as a legacy to my country. And never forget Horatia." Then, Nelson drew the chaplain close and as he died he whispered very distinctly so that all those present heard, "Thank God I have done my duty."

Sometime later an unknown individual recorded in the ship's log, "Partial firing continued until 4:30 when a victory having been reported to the Right Hon. Lord Viscount Nelson, K. B., and Commander-in-Chief, he died of his wound." The final victory had been won.

Sedan

by Angela Stuart

As the poet, Alfred de Musset, was descending a staircase in the Tuileries during a Second Empire ball, he said, "It is all very beautiful—for the moment, but I would not give two sous for the last act."

The curtain rose on the last act of the Second Empire, July 19, 1870, when France declared war on Prussia. It fell September 1, 1870, in a small fortified town in the blood-soaked northeastern corner of France, by the name of Sedan.

In lists of crucial battles there are the Blenheims and the Solferinos, noted for inordinate slaughter; others like Leuthen and Rossbach are masterpieces of strategy. But whether from a tactical, strategic, historical or psychological standpoint, only two battles are bald synonyms for defeat—Waterloo and Sedan.

To the English, and by imitation, the Americans, "he met his Waterloo" has never ceased to be a statement of irretrievable ruin. But not to the French. To them it was a defeat, but with mitigations. Although Napoleon was opposed by almost every army in Europe, he came close to winning in Belgium. France could console herself that by Wellington's own admission, Waterloo was "a damned nice thing—the nearest run thing you ever saw in your life."

But for Sedan there were no consolations. It was a debacle, a defeat without even the halo of *La Gloire*. After the surrender the Emperor Napoleon III and an army of a quarter of a million men were taken captive by the Germans. French pride was crushed. The world awoke with a start to the results of the lightning six-week campaign; namely, an upstart German state had shattered the leading power on the Continent, and an army which had been the model for Europe since Charlemagne was in shackles.

There can be no doubt Sedan affected the destinies of nations far beyond the actual conflict. Because it destroyed one empire and laid the foundations of another, the outcome of the battle left both the map and the moral order of Europe revolutionized. France's traditional role of being the prime center of European power was lost, never to be regained. The lethal course of Franco-German relations dates from Sedan.

But the great majority of the French people were vouchsafed no such glimpse over the rim of their own century into the next, where the battle had already sown the seeds of two world wars in "the wide arable land of events." For them the issues were far simpler. Under Napoleon III there had been much to enjoy. When he fell to the Germans at Sedan there was much to regret.

It has often been said the truest explanation for the battle of Sedan is that Napoleon III was not Napoleon I.

It is only fair to add that if the emperor in 1870 had had one marshal of the caliber of the six or seven who surrounded his famous uncle, the nadir of the surrender at Sedan might never have been reached. From first to last the life of Louis Napoleon, who became emperor of the French, was ruled by a great name. Throughout his reign, futile analogies and sterile comparisons with the colossal stature of the first Napoleon were continually at work to undermine his prestige.

Between the Napoleonic ideal and the heart of France, a dark, profound and indissoluble unity has always existed. It is no mere epigram that France loves peace but prefers glory. When Louis Napoleon became the head of the French state, he was the heir to the Bonaparte legend with all its crude exaltation of military adventure. Because of his origins he was forced to keep France dazzled. And although his government was modern, peace-minded, and democratic, he could no more eliminate the Napoleonic legend than Prussia could cast off the ruthless cynicism of Frederick the Great.

Now, after a century's perspective, there has been a revision in the traditional picture of Napoleon III—that of the elderly rake with waxed mustaches, heavy lids, lackluster eyes, who swindled his way to the throne but collapsed at the stern touch of reality. It is true that he had no dash, but beneath his physical uncouthness was an uncontested personal charm, a warm and deep benevolence. As a small prince, whenever he was approached by a mendicant, his charity took the disconcerting form of immediately stripping off his clothes and handing them over. It was an instinctive response to suffering and want which he never outgrew.

Throughout his reign, he would be profoundly devoted to the cause of the masses, the inarticulate, the humble, the forgotten. In this he stands almost unique in the long line of French sovereigns. "By comparison,"

Bismarck (right) sits with a dejected Napoleon III the day after Sedan. (PIX)

The German victory at Metz on August 18, 1870. (PIX)

Kaiser Wilhelm watches the victory parade at Longchamp, Paris, March 3, 1871. (PIX)

as his biographer Guérard points out, "the truly glorious rulers, Francis I, Richelieu, Louis XIV, Napoleon I, are cold and harsh. They prized France merely as their pedestal."

While the most famous victories of Napoleon I are carved on the base of the *Arc de Triomphe,* it is less widely known that the International Red Cross owes its life to the stubborn championship of Napoleon III against tremendous difficulties.

Europe laughed at his idea of congresses to settle disputes among nations by arbitration. But in his approach to foreign policy he was centuries ahead of Bismarck—a man not of his own age so much as ours. The things he labored for, confusedly, haltingly—all nationalities free and equal within a united Europe, industrial wealth for the many—were utopias yesterday. They are still utopias today.

Prince Louis Napoleon was twice over a Bonaparte since he was the son of Napoleon's brother, King Louis of Holland, and of Queen Hortense, daughter of the empress Josephine. There had always been a close bond of affection between Napoleon and his stepdaughter. In flight from Waterloo, he rushed into the chateau of Malmaison where Hortense was staying with her two small sons, to bid a last, hasty adieu.

Upon his nephew, Louis Napoleon, who was seven, the emperor conferred the star and the cordon of the Legion of Honour, hugged him, and was gone.

For the prince, the moment was enshrined. He would grow up under the inspiration of the Napoleonic legend, confirmed in a passionate faith in his star, his destiny. But during the years he was a Bonapartist pretender, he alone was to believe in the star. Banished from his country, he suffered penury, want, and ridicule. "Napoleon's cocked hat with no brains under it," his enemies called him.

In 1840 Louis Napoleon made an attempt to invade

France, crossing the Channel with a few supporters in a small steamer with a live eagle tied to the mast. The coup came to nothing. The prince was tried for his life and condemned to perpetual imprisonment in the fortress of Ham. Even the eagle was captured and would have been sent to the slaughter house except that a peasant with Bonapartist leanings purchased him. For months afterward, coup and mascot were the laughing stock of the European press.

But, if nothing else, captivity served to make the prince a man of letters. Once, under the empire, when someone expressed surprise at the extent of his learning, he replied, "You forget my years at the University of Ham."

After six years' imprisonment, he applied to the government to repair his quarters. They obligingly sent in laborers; whereupon Louis Napoleon, dressed in the clothes of a mason, and carrying a plank in front of his face, managed to escape from the moated fortress.

He fled to England and in 1848, the fateful year of revolution, he reappeared in France. This time, by the magic of his name, he was elected president of the new republic by plebiscite of five-and-a-half million votes. There was a saying: "Paris goes her own way. France irritated, is forced to follow." But in the case of the Bonapartist pretender, it was the rural electorate who raised him to supreme power. Better than anyone else, he represented the French peasantry whose hearts were on the right, but whose pockets were on the left.

At the time of his election, he was already forty and had spent half his life as an outlaw. But faith in his star was finally vindicated. Within three years he had overwhelmed all adversaries and by consummate political machinations made himself absolute. Karl Marx was moved to prophesy: "If the Imperial mantle should, in the end, fall upon the shoulders of Louis Bonaparte, the iron statue of Napoleon will crash from the top of the Vendome column."

By the coup d'état of December 2, 1852, Louis Napoleon was proclaimed emperor of the French, but the Vendome statue did not crash. The empire came about so naturally as to seem inevitable. It was the shadowy, transcendental heritage of a name.

When Louis Napoleon, while still prince-president, made trips to the provinces, he was hailed "Vive Napoleon!" Printed notices read "Vive Napoleon!!!" The transition from the three exclamation marks to "Vive Napoleon III" was a simple matter.

A wave of economic expansion followed the establishment of the empire. When Napoleon II came to the throne there were few big concentrations either of labor or capital. He recognized at once that new banks were needed for the growth of industry. To meet this need and to make wealth more flexible, he invented credit in its modern form. Under his patronage mighty banking concerns like the Crédit Lyonnais and the Crédit Foncier were founded which provided funds for the mechanization of factories and a subsequent increase in production.

In particular, the emperor's new credit allowed for the improvement of communications by road, rail and water. In the short duration of the empire, the railway network increased from 3,685 kilometers to 179,244, and the foreign commerce of France was trebled.

At the advent of the Second Empire it was the fashion for more legitimate monarchs to scoff at Napoleon III as a prestigious upstart. Leopold I complained that having the Bonapartist upon the French throne was like waking up and finding oneself in bed with a snake. You didn't dare move for fear of disturbing the creature.

Napoleon III was undoubtedly an enigma in politics, "the sphinx of the Tuileries," who usually kept his ministers in the dark as to his intentions. From his past as a conspirator he retained a fondness for devious sources of information, personal contacts and mysterious interviews. But because he had known the vicissitudes of a pretender, he was far more enlightened as to the needs and cravings of the helpless masses of the people than any of his fellow rulers who were born to the purple. His most far-reaching reforms were for the working class—the section of France for which he strove hardest.

He projected shorter working hours and health legislation; set up institutions of maternal welfare to replace the drunken midwife, and homes for injured workers. Under the empire, loathsome prison hulks were abolished and the right to strike granted.

But the most enduring landmark of the Second Empire was the rebuilding of Paris. Acting through his agent, Baron Haussmann, the emperor directed great boulevards to be cut through the evil-smelling higgledy-piggledy alleys of old Paris, and the city essentially as it stands today was born.

To improve sanitation Haussmann created a vast system of underground drainage away from the Seine. It was so widely publicized that for decades a visit to the sewers of Paris was a tourist attraction.

In the economic area Napoleon III achieved a startling success, which gave the lie to detractors such as Karl Marx who held the motto of the Second Empire should not be "Liberty, Equality and Fraternity," but "Cavalry, Infantry and Artillery." It can safely be said France has never known such contented years as the two glittering decades between the coup d'état of December 2, 1852, and Sedan.

On the last day in June, 1870, the English foreign secretary, looking out at the political horizon, said he could not discern "a cloud in the sky."

Simultaneously, Emile Ollivier, the French premier, boasted to the deputies that "never in history was the maintenance of peace in Europe so certainly assured."

This was on Thursday. Sunday evening a telegram reached Paris that brought an electric thrill of war. According to the wire, Bismarck, the Prussian chancellor, had sent a secret messenger to Madrid about placing a Hohenzollern prince on the vacant throne of Spain. If the plan succeeded it meant France would be hemmed in between two Hohenzollern princes, so she was bound to prevent the negotiation.

A few Paris journalists argued that fear of encirclement was far-fetched since the candidate—Leopold of Hohenzollern—Sigmaringen was of the Swabian branch of the family which had been separated for centuries from the Prussian. But in France the mere name Hohenzollern, regardless of what branch, was a red flag to a bull. Besides, Prince Leopold was a colonel in the Prussian army; he lived much at the court of Berlin, and his sympathies were with the German movement of the time.

Early in July, King William of Prussia was at the little watering-place of Ems, taking the cure. Benedetti, the French ambassador to Prussia, was ordered to hasten to Ems where "he should endeavor to persuade the king to issue *an order* to the prince of Hohenzollern to abandon the candidature."

Benedetti was received most cordially by the Prussian monarch. But in reply to the ambassador's demand, His Majesty said that in his quality of king of Prussia he knew absolutely nothing of this candidature; that as head of the Hohenzollern family it was true that he was aware of it, but that he had no right to order Prince Hohenzollern, who was of full age, either to accept or to refuse the Spanish crown, which he therefore declined doing.

In Paris, the truculent foreign secretary, the duc de Gramont, fumed with impatience. "If the King will not counsel the Hohenzollern Prince to renounce," he wrote to Benedetti, "well, it is war at once and in a few days we shall be on the Rhine."

At this point, Prince Leopold, hearing of the complications that had arisen, and not wanting to be the cause of war between France and Germany, abandoned the candidature. On July 12, telegrams announcing his renunciation were received at the French foreign office. To all intents and purposes the incident was closed.

It was a diplomatic victory for France, but Gramont proved unappeasable. He telephoned Benedetti that he should exact from King William a guarantee that His Majesty would never again allow the prince to be a candidate for the throne of Spain. This was asking the king to give a promise as to an eventuality that was hardly his affair, and he positively refused.

In July, 1870, as in July, 1914, there was a spate of crucial wires. Hour by hour telegraphy recorded the mounting tension.

On the evening of July 13, Von Roon, Prussian minister of war, and Von Moltke, chief of staff, were dining with Bismarck in Berlin. During dinner a telegraph arrived in which King William gave an account of the French ambassador's pressing demands and their final rejection. The king suggested that Bismarck communicate the contents of the wire to the press and the Prussian embassies. There was no instruction to publish the exact words. Bismarck, after discussing the matter with the two war lords, made a terse summary, touching up the message in such a way as to give it an insulting tone—as though the king had peremptorily dismissed the French ambassador.

The doctored text of the Ems telegram was inserted at once in an extra edition of the *Nord Agemeine Zeitung,* and by morning there was a copy in every foreign capital. On July 14, the German ambassador presented himself at the French Ministry to announce that he had received orders to demand his passports and to quit France. Immediate war could not be averted.

In defining the function of a statesman Bismarck once said he should lie in wait "until he hears the step of God sounding through events and then spring forward and seize the hem of his garment." In the case of the Ems telegram, Bismarck made a mighty lunge, and what he seized was the future destiny of Europe.

Boiled down, the crisis over the Spanish succession amounted to this: Bismarck had known all along that Napoleon would not and could not tolerate a second Prussia beyond the Pyrenees—one beyond the Rhine was more than enough. The project of seating a Hohenzollern prince on the vacant throne of Spain meant war with France. Since German unity required a German war, it was not unwelcome. Von Moltke was ready and it was better to fight the French before they found their allies.

As far back as the Great Paris Exhibition of 1867 there had been disquieting portents in the air. Into the midst of the newest marvels from the realms of art, science and industry ranged on the Champs-de-Mars, the Germans had hauled their single exhibit—a fifty-ton gun by Herr Krupp which fired a one-thousand-pound shell. Because it was the biggest armament the world had ever seen, it won a prize. But the Parisians ignored the squat black monster with its ominous snout, while flocking to look at the new patent piece of American furniture known as a rocking chair.

They were equally indifferent to the sight of Prussian officers with mutton chop whiskers hovering over the detailed relief maps of all the great French fortresses so obligingly placed on display. To the French of the Second Empire, who looked upon themselves as the heirs of Richelieu, Louis XIV and Napoleon I, Bismarck's Germans were "those ridiculous Teutons." Paris, far from taking fright at Herr Krupp's products, laughed at an army under the command of a "General Boum."

On July 19, the king of Prussia received from the French charge d'affaires the formal declaration of war. Immediately France was branded a frivolous aggressor without friend or ally. In the eyes of the rest of Europe her nagging persistence in the matter of the Spanish candidature, when the incident was so obviously closed, looked like a wanton provocation to war. The *Illustrated London News* announced, "The Liberal Empire goes to war on a mere point of etiquette."

The man in the street was inclined to agree with Ruskin, who wrote of the two belligerents: "The constitution of their governments and the clumsy crookedness of their political dealings with each other, may be such as to prevent either of them from knowing the actual cause for which they have gone to war."

But across the Rhine there were no doubts. Patriotism was fired to a fever pitch by the memory of fourteen French invasions of Germany which had taken place between 1785 and 1813—to say nothing of the recurrent meddling of France in German affairs for the past two hundred years. The whole of Bonn University, one thousand students, joined the colors.

Under the Prussian system of universal service, and because reserves were organized on a regional basis far in advance of the era, the German states were able to raise an army of 1,183,000 men within 18 days of mobilization. Nothing on this scale had ever been seen before. Von Moltke had devoted his entire genius to the creation of the general staff, recruited from the elite of Potsdam, to form the brain and nerves of this great body of troops.

Railways built in Germany had been planned with an eye to military needs; a highly trained corps of telegraphers ensured excellent communications. All aimed at a maximum speed of concentration for an offensive campaign that would hit the enemy hard before he was ready. It was a technique Germany would copy in two later European wars.

The French army went to war trailing clouds of glory, but little else. To counteract Germany's known superiority in numbers, the French minister of war, Le Boeuf, strove for extreme rapidity of movement. To that end he introduced a radical change in the system of mobilization. Units were to be rushed to the frontier just as they stood, while the quota of men, horses, and materials required to bring them to war strength, were to be hurried after them.

The result was indescribable chaos. Mobilization broke down completely as the whole nation surged with men traveling frenetically to and fro. On the third day of mobilization General Micheler telegraphed Paris in despair: "Have arrived at Belfort. Can't find my brigade. Can't find the divisional commander. What shall I do? Don't know where my regiments are."

When travel-weary troops reached their destination there was often nowhere to sleep because their tents could not be found. Magazines were discovered to be empty. Gunners became separated from their guns. In Metz, France's chief war depot, there were no stores of sugar, coffee, brandy or rice, and worst of all, no salt. At Douai a gunner general reported, "Found a fine stock of horse-collars, but one-third of them were too narrow to fit any animal's neck."

Emile Zola, summing up the horrible improvidence with which France went so gaily to war in 1870, wrote of "a Germany ready, better commanded, better armed, sublimated by a great charge of patriotism; France frightened, delivered into disorder—having neither the leaders nor the men nor the necessary arms."

From the border marches of Alsace and Lorraine

there are endless views to east and west over the Gauls and the Germanies. Here, in eastern France, the historic battleground in the contest between two rival civilizations, the French and Prussian forces converged in the golden autumn days of the "Terrible Year."

On July 28, Napoleon arrived at the fortress of Metz to assume command of his armies. Ferdinand Foche, who was 18, saw the emperor as he passed through the town and said later that he gave the impression "of a man utterly worn out." But few were aware that his condition was critical.

A short time before there had been a consultation of eminent doctors at St. Cloud. They had diagnosed that Napoleon had a stone in the bladder "large as a pigeon's egg." It was recommended that he should avoid all forms of fatigue and on no account ride on horseback. In short, he was more suited for an operation than a campaign. But the doctors' report had not been communicated to the government, or even the empress, for fear of causing alarm.

Napoleon was immediately disillusioned by the shortage of materials—Metz was calling for a million rations—and by the weak complement of the units. Incredible as it might seem, not a single French army corps was at full strength.

Von Moltke had 400,000 men in supreme fighting trim and 1,440 guns concentrated on the far side of the Rhine, against the less than 250,000 partially organized men Napoleon had been able to muster. The French had a distinct advantage in their cartridge-firing chasepot rifle with nearly twice the range of the Prussian "needlegun" and greater rapidity of fire. But in the field of artillery they had nothing to compare with the steel, breech-loading cannon which Herr Krupp had presented at the Great Exhibition. While French shells tended to burst noisily but harmlessly in the air, Prussian percussion shells exploded with devastating effect when they made contact with their target.

Under the emperor's supreme command the two main armies were entrusted to Marshal MacMahon, the duke of Magenta and to Marshal Bazaine, who had commanded the ill-fated Mexican campaign. Napoleon's plan was for Bazaine's army to hold the Prussians in Lorraine, while MacMahon advanced rapidly eastward into Germany in hopes of swinging the South German kingdoms and eventually the reluctant Austrians into the war against Prussia. But it was too late for any such strategy. The South Germans, cowed and docile, were rapidly mobilizing under Von Moltke's orders.

The first battles were fought on the frontier, and France, due to the weakness of her units, was at once invaded. At this stage Paris was swept by contradictory rumors. One minute universal rejoicing broke out at news of some miraculous success, or that the king of Prussia had gone mad. There was an immediate rush to the windows to hang out flags and light lamps. Half an hour later another dispatch would arrive, and away went the flags and out went the lamps.

While foreign diplomats were discussing the illumination of the embassies for the French entry into Berlin, disaster struck. Eugenie took chloral in an empty palace and Paris stared at the account of the battle of Worth by which MacMahon had lost Alsace and one of France's two armies to the enemy.

At Metz the general met to discuss plans. There were fierce altercations over strategy, but all agreed upon one point. The emperor must relinquish his command. He had failed to cross the Rhine; instead, the Prussians now had one foot in la belle France, and against him in Lorraine were advancing three German armies, each one stronger than his own.

On August 13, as Prussian Uhlans were beginning to trot into startled villages, Napoleon handed over to Bazaine the remnants of his supreme command. In taking leave of the marshal, he said: "I entrust to you the last army of France. Think of the Prince Imperial."

He planned to return to Paris, but Eugenie, who was acting as regent, wired that on no account must he show up in the capital with his forces bearing the stigma of defeat. To the man whose name was Napoleon that was clear.

After the early defeats at Spicheren and Worth the French never again left the defensive—a form of combat for which they were wholly unsuited. Often irresistible in attack when fired by the spirit of *furia Francese,* they have never been good at the kind of slogging withdrawal in which the British soldier excels. It was August, the blood-month in European annals, when the imperial armies began their long disheartening retreat —away from the cherished goal of the Rhine and back into France.

On August 16, Napoleon arrived at Chalons where MacMahon had withdrawn with his shredded forces. Out of the debris, and raw levies from Paris, he was striving feverishly to constitute a new army. The emperor held a council of war with his marshal and a highly important decision was reached—to retire with the whole army upon Paris and take up a defensive position slightly in advance of the capital. It was the same type of operation which brought the Allies victory in the First World War when Foche made his famous announcement, "Gentlemen, we will fight on the Marne."

While no "miracle of the Marne" was to be expected in 1870—the imperial armies were too outclassed—the front could have been stabilized. This achieved, the friendly neutrals, Austria and Italy, might have helped to set up the peace terms. But Eugenie was quick to cancel the plan, wiring that neither the ministers nor the populace would tolerate any such retirement.

Above all, the emperor must keep away from Paris.

As for MacMahon, the government made a decision for him, also. He was told to lead his army out and join that of Bazaine who was about to be encircled in the fortress of Metz. Many historians consider this the most fatal decision of the whole war. Napoleon himself described it as a move contrary to all the principles of strategy and common sense.

MacMahon recognized the extreme difficulty of reaching Metz because the Prussian crown prince's columns were astride his route in great strength. Nevertheless, he started out, following by-paths that led into the forest wilderness of the Argonne. The emperor, the white elephant of the campaign, trailed along in the dust of the army. As the weather changed, the roads became wet and terribly congested. Provisioning broke down.

The imperial equipage and baggage train with their splendid teams of draught animals, the coachmen and outriders glittering profusely in gold and scarlet, were in stark contrast to the dejected mood of the weary, half-famished troops. Napoleon himself sat crouching in the corner of his carriage, seemingly impervious to the miseries around him, but actually suffering spasms of pain at every jolt which moved the stone in his bladder.

When MacMahon passed into the broad valley of the Meuse he hardly knew where he was. Neither he nor any of his generals had a map of the French terrain—only maps of Germany. Of these copious German maps, a general wired Paris that they were *"inutiles pour le moment."*

On August 30, MacMahon's army stopped to rest at Beaumont-sur-Meuse, still sixty miles from his objective, Metz. As the village church chimed the Angelus, German shells began falling among the French troops. When Von Moltke's reconnaissance had first told him of

MacMahon's maneuver, the German chief of staff was incredulous that the French would throw away their only mobile army in a futile attempt to pry Bazaine out of Metz, while the eastern route to Paris via Verdun lay open and undefended.

Throughout the campaign the Prussians had often been nonplussed by the absurdity of the enemy's moves. What they did not know was that the strategy of the French armies in the field was in the hands of civilian ministers who had never been so much as astride a horse.

Von Moltke promptly sent powerful forces to bar the French advance. The ensuing battle of Beaumont was indecisive, and at quarter to ten that night the emperor boarded a northbound train. It was so ancient they dared not light a lamp. As Napoleon smoked incessantly, nothing was visible in the dark except the fiery tip of his cigarette.

Toward midnight, when the rumbling carriages arrived at their destination, the engine driver opened the door of the emperor's compartment.

"Sire," he said, "we are at Sedan."

Sedan, a small grey town with fifteenth century fortifications, lies deep in the valley of the Meuse. Around it in a rough oval are heights and woods, ideal for battery emplacements. The town with its narrow streets and houses wedged tightly together, with hardly an open space, was obviously a vulnerable enclosure.

But all the same, on August 31, MacMahon withdrew there from Beaumont with his shattered and demoralized army of 90,000 men. (The town normally accommodated 15,000 people.) Later, MacMahon explained his move to a Parliamentary Commission: "The truth is that I did not reckon on fighting a battle on the ground we occupied. I knew already that we had no provisions and that the place was barely supplied with munitions, but I did not yet know on which side I ought, on the morrow (September 1) to effect my retreat."

As a matter of fact, issues from Sedan were all difficult, being in the nature of defiles which can only be traversed slowly, even in time of peace, by large bodies of men, horses, guns and weapons.

The French have always shown great skill in building fortresses, and at this point in the war they had cooped themselves up in two—Metz and Sedan. The battle that took place at Sedan would follow the favorite French formula of an army backed by a citadel. While for the Germans, who have always liked above everything else to encircle the enemy and hug him to death, it was an opportunity made to order.

The only hope for the French lay in strongly holding the heights surrounding Sedan, with artillery. But during the day and night of August 31, while MacMahon rested his troops and tried to provide them with food and ammunition, the Prussian army crossed the Meuse above and below Sedan, and commenced to occupy the heights which commanded the town.

In the Prussian camp, on the night of August 31, King William's orders to his son, the crown prince, were to march at dawn and attack the enemy wherever he could be found on the left and right banks of the Meuse, "in order that he might be crushed up as much as possible between the river and the Belgian border."

Consistently, French cavalry reconnaissance had made the tragic error of failing to patrol far enough. On the fateful eve of battle, they rode, as usual, only a short distance out from Sedan, so they neither saw nor heard the nearest German corps as it struggled through the woods.

At four o'clock on the morning of September 1 the Bavarians moved cautiously through a thick mist that filled the valley of the Meuse. Two miles out of Sedan they collided with the French at the village of Bazeilles, and the daylong battle began.

As the Germans closed in through the wooded terrain and occupied villages, the French infantry fought fiercely to dislodge them, but they could not endure the thick, ceaseless hail of shells from the terrible batteries on the high ground. The French artillery, brave and devoted, went into action. However, since the Germans had taken so many of the heights, the converging fire from the hostile hills blew up the French tumbrils, sometimes two at once, killed or wounded the gunners and swept away the horses.

Inside the French lines MacMahon was severely wounded between 7 and 8 a.m. and turned the command of the army over to General Ducrot. Ducrot, an excellent officer, immediately ordered a retreat on Mezières to save at least part of his forces. The retreat had already begun in good order when a newcomer, General de Wimpffen, appeared with a letter from Paris authorizing him to take command in case MacMahon were disabled.

He immediately cancelled the order to withdraw. As the Germans came on in irresistible waves the two generals engaged in a conflict on the battlefield that destroyed the last chance of either a defense or a retreat.

Meanwhile, the emperor was with the French artillery on the hills above La Moncelle. Always a first-rate horseman, he rode in agony at Sedan. Later, the English surgeon, Sir Henry Thompson, marveled how he could have remained five hours on horseback while under fire. "The pain which he must have endured is indescribable."

Napoleon had rouged his cheeks that his troops would not take fright at his critical condition. This was the origin of the derisive legend of the "painted Emperor" galloping over the heights above Sedan while the last army of France reeled backward in defeat.

A Prussian infantry battalion storms a French position on Roten Berg (Red Hill). (PIX)

In the valley, at every point of attack, the German troops "were thrown into the fight like coal on a fire." By one o'clock the encirclement of the French army was complete. No fewer than 426 guns were hailing shells upon the unfortunate French who were almost piled one upon another in an area which did not measure two miles either in depth or breadth. Herr Krupp with the brilliant marksmanship of the German gunners, in particular the Saxons, was winning the day. At this stage, General Ducrot made a desperate appeal to the cavalry to try and punch a hole in the German lines through which the French infantry might pass in retreat.

The response was magnificent. On the hillsides south of Floring and on the lowlands bordering the Meuse, the whole of the French cavalry, with Salignac Fenelor's lancers in the front, swooped down upon the enemy like a hurricane and broke through the line of Prussian skirmishers. But they were received by the deployed battalions with a point-blank fire so murderous that the French squadrons were literally mowed down.

The charges under the command of General Gallifet were renewed with a gallantry worthy of the First Empire. General Gallifet's entrails were kept in his body by a silver plate placed there by surgeons because of a wound he had received in Mexico. But to Ducrot's question, would the cavalry try yet again, Gallifet is reported to have replied: "As often as you like, *mon général*, as often as there's one of us left!"

For a third time they charged, only to be shattered by the German guns, but this time drawing forth praise from the watching king of Prussia: "Ah! The brave fellows!" Words that are carved on the memorial above Floring.

Even after the cavalry, having failed to make a gap in the German encirclement, was driven back in disorder, the French army remained heroically stubborn in its resistance to inevitable fate.

According to German "Staff History," a powerful artillery fire directed against the enemy's last point of refuge appeared the most suitable method of convincing him of the hopelessness of his situation. At four in the afternoon, to hasten the capitulation and to spare the German army further sacrifices, the king ordered the whole available artillery to concentrate its fire on Sedan.

The results of the reinforced and concentrated shell fire were soon apparent. Sedan seemed in flames. The French return fire, gallantly maintained for a short time, was presently crushed into silence.

Inside the invested city, Napoleon saw that with the bombardment crashing down upon his trapped soldiers, there was no alternative between massacre or surrender. Assuming once more his sovereign authority, he gave the order at five o'clock to hoist a white flag on the citadel. The German fire ceased at once.

When Prussian officers penetrated the city to arrange for the surrender, to their immense surprise they were ushered into the presence of Napoleon. The German high command had not the slightest notion that in capturing an army they had also bagged the emperor of the French.

The Prussian envoys went trotting back up the hill to their headquarters in a state of intense excitement. As they came to an encampment of troops, one officer ponited backwards toward Sedan, shouting, "*Der Kaiser ist da!*" at which there was a tremendous outburst of cheering.

According to the protocol of capitulation signed September 2, "The French Army, placed under the orders of General de Wimpffen, finding itself actually surrounded in Sedan by superior forces, is *prisoner of war.*"

The outstanding fact at Sedan was that the French

were vastly outnumbered. On the day of surrender the contending forces were: French 80,000–Germans 220,000. The French had rations for only one day.

It was settled that the emperor would be held in captivity in Castle Wilhelmshohe in Bavaria. On September 3, he set out with his suite in a heavy downpour of rain. On September 5, when the train made its last stop in France at Verviers, Napoleon learned from a newspaper sold to him on the station platform that he was no longer emperor of the French.

During the term of his imprisonment, Louis Napoleon showed the inner greatness which, despite a long record of sensualities and intrigues, he had somehow managed to preserve. France, her Gallic pride cut to the quick by the terms of the surrender, was calling him a poltroon because he had not buried himself, his dynasty and his army under the rubble at Sedan. The revolutionary press in Paris was taking it hard that he was still alive and enjoying the relative comfort of internment in a German castle.

But as Napoleon had once said, "To be slandered is a prince's business," and he expressed no rancor. Instead, all his humanity was devoted to alleviating the sufferings of the soldiers for whom he had capitulated. He had distributed most of his funds among them before he left Sedan, and from Bismarck he extracted a guarantee that they would be adequately cared for during the severe German winter. He even interceded with his captors for the life of a stray dog which had followed him in the castle park, offering all sorts of sums to keep him fed.

A prisoner of war, he still followed every move of the peace negotiations at Versailles. From distant Wilhelmshohe he solicited Bismarck that Belfort be preserved to France, "lest enemies should make it a loaded revolver aimed at her heart." And that neither the French battleships nor Algeria should be forfeited.

Concessions which the chancellor granted.

As the direct outcome of Sedan, according to the treaty of Frankfurt signed May 10, 1871, France lost Alsace and Lorraine in which were included the great fortresses of Metz and Strasburg, and was compelled to pay an indemnity of two billion dollars.

Of even greater import to the future of the world, Bismarck made his king an emperor amid the mirrors at Versailles.

After Napoleon's release from Wilhelmshohe, he joined Eugenie and his son, the prince imperial, in a quiet English country house at Chiselhurst. Here the vanquished emperor reverted to his old design which had evoked incredulous smiles from Queen Victoria and Palmerston—the idea of a congress, or rather a league of nations. "An international Council to watch over the affairs of Europe, to follow and study the various phases which the relation of state to state might assume, and to interpret and explain treaties."

It was to be the subject of his last book, but death intervened on January 9, 1873. A hundred years later we are still striving to implement the aims of this prince who loved to say, "It is civil war to fight in Europe."

sceaux.

En foi de quoi les soussignés ont revêtu le présent traité préliminaire de leurs signatures et de leurs sceaux.

Fait à Versailles le 26 février 1871.

v. Bismarck A. Thiers

Jules Favre

Les Royaumes de Bavière et de Wurtemberg et le Grand Duché de Bade ayant pris part à la guerre actuelle comme alliés de la Prusse et faisant partie maintenant de l'Empire Germanique, les soussignés adhèrent à la présente convention au nom de leurs souverains respectifs.

Versailles, le 26 février, 1871.

Cte. de Bray-Steinburg
B. de Waechter
Mittnacht
Jolly

The second page of the preliminary peace treaty signed at Versailles February 26, 1871. (PIX)

The Siege of Paris

by Angela Stuart

On September 2, 1870, the day France's last army in the field capitulated to the Prussians at Sedan, Napoleon III sent a letter of one line to the Empress Eugenie in the Tuileries: *"Elle est complète."*

Unfortunately for France, nothing was finished, the end was not even in sight. Bismarck would have been glad to stop the campaign there and then and to arrange for terms of peace on the battlefield. He quite naturally considered an emperor with an army a more stable contracting party than a chamber of noisy, gesticulating deputies. The terms of an immediate treaty would have been harsh since the defeat was unprecedented, but not so crushing as they were to prove four months later when German tempers were exacerbated by French stubbornness.

The tragedy for Napoleon at Sedan was that he had made so many liberal concessions in the last years of his reign and undermined his authority to such an extent, he was powerless to negotiate a peace. It was only his personal sword that he surrendered to Wilhelm I of Prussia on the hill of La Marfée above Sedan. He could not speak for Paris. So the ink had hardly dried on the protocol of capitulation before Von Moltke was wheeling his vast forces around the cries of "*Nacht Paris!*"

Meanwhile, in the capital, events moved with lightning rapidity. On 4 September there was an uprising against the regime, and the empress fled, accompanied by a single lady-in-waiting, without any luggage except two lawn handkerchiefs. She had a severe cold. But it has never been the practice of the Paris revolutionary to give deposed royalty time to pack. Louis-Philippe left the Tuileries in the middle of a meal, which the mob, bursting into the palace, finished for him.

A government of national defense was hastily formed in the Hotel de Ville, seat of those transitory governments Paris was always raising up from the pavements during the Great Revolution. However, in 1870 the new regime was composed of Republican moderates who had come to terms, for the moment, with the extreme Left. Offices were filled by the simple expedient of writing a candidate's name on a slip of paper and throwing it out the window to the crowd that surged in the Place de Ville. If the response was wildly vociferous, he was elected. As usual, it was a government "by Parisians, of Parisians and for Parisians." The provinces were not even consulted.

General Trochu, whose name was repeatedly called out by the mob, was appointed president of the new republic, and so became the "Man of September 4th." Paris saw nothing paradoxical in this fad of dating its idols. (Louis-Napoleon had been the "Man of December 10th"—when the coup d'etat in 1851 established the empire.) Trochu, a Breton, a Catholic and an extremely able soldier, won the confidence of the Republicans because he had made no effort to save the empire and was one of the few military leaders whose reputation was untarnished by Sedan.

All in all, it was the most joyous revolution Paris had ever had. The *Marseillaise,* forbidden under the empire, blared out night and day on the boulevards. The rifles of the national guard carried bouquets, and red crepe paper fluttered from the lamp-posts. Like the supernumeraries in an opera, the mob acted on cue, rushing around to efface all the symbols of the last dynasty. The imperial eagles went the way of the former Bourbon lilies. The "N's" which Rostand predicted would give the "No!" to time, were chiseled and ripped off the pediments of public monuments, the busts of Napoleon III were gleefully hurled into the Seine.

The stolid Teutons were astonished by this indestructible French buoyancy. By all rational counts Prussia was victorious, France vanquished. But even while German phalanxes were closing in upon the capital with inexorable speed, Paris had all the appearances of being *en fete*.

While jubilation reigned, President Trochu, charged with the defense of Paris against the advance of the spiked helmets, took grim count of his assets. The only major unit left to France was General Vinoy's newly formed XIII Corps. It had been too slow to reach Sedan and so had come straggling back to Paris, weary and demoralized. A bric-a-brac of other troops, escaped from Sedan and elsewhere, raised the total of regulars inside the capital to around 60,000. This was augmented by a force of 100,000 young Mobiles; raw Territorials who had received only the sketchiest training.

In addition to this nucleus of regular army troops and Territorials, there was the Paris National Guard—about to win undying fame for reasons quite outside the defense of Paris. The wartime strength of the *Garde* had been 90,000. When the government of national defense decided to expand it by compulsory registration, everyone was amazed that the enrollment produced some 350,000 able-bodied males. The municipal guardsmen were never intended for use in combat, except to relieve the regulars on the fortifications. So what to do with this great mass of untrained civilians bearing arms, posed a problem to the regular army. As Goncourt, the faithful scribe of the siege, noted in his journal: "Everybody who eats or drinks outside the cabarets holds a rifle between his knees."

In all, Paris had a defense force of a half million. "Plenty of men," as Trochu said, "but few soldiers."

The city's only real hope of surviving the siege lay in its external fortifications. The whole of Paris was surrounded by an *enceinte* wall, thirty feet high and divided into ninety-three bastions linked by masonry "curtains." In front of the wall was a moat ten feet wide and behind ran a circular railway for supplying troops to the ramparts. Beyond the moat, at distances varying from one to three miles, was a chain of sixteen powerful forts. Each one mounted fifty to seventy heavy guns and was in a superbly commanding position.

To supplement his interior defense, Trochu set 12,000 laborers to work digging earthworks in weak places and laying electrically fired land mines. The beautiful trees in the Bois were felled to make barricades, and houses on the outskirts of Paris ruthlessly demolished to improve fields of fire. Seldom had a city been so strongly fortified.

As for foodstuffs, the government had amassed great quantities on the hoof. The Bois de Boulogne was "a sea of wool" with some 250,000 sheep turned loose to graze, as well as 40,000 oxen. Even the city squares had their smaller animals nibbling the grass. In the forest around Paris, public hunts had been carried out to prevent any game from falling into Prussian hands, while a steady stream of carts hauled all that was edible from nearby market gardens into the capital.

The approach of the siege brought one unforeseen development. Not only refugees and escaped soldiers crowded into Paris, but the trains brought a great influx of foreigners—chiefly British and American—with a taste for excitement. These outsiders arrived so thick and fast, one Paris real estate agent advertised: "Notice for the benefit of English gentlemen wishing to attend the Siege of Paris. Comfortable apartments, completely shell-proof; rooms in the basement for impressionable persons."

As a result, the defense government, instead of having its estimated 1,500,000 inhabitants to feed, ended up with considerably over 2,000,000. In mid-September, the preparations for the siege being complete, the world was presented with the curious spectacle of a nineteenth-century capital withdrawing inside its keep and leaving the rest of the country to the mercy of the marauders.

By 1870 advances in artillery had greatly altered the classical forms of warfare. Gone was the "sweet and sunny fighting" of Sir Walter Scott's heroes. Still, the aim of any army in the field was the same as in the eighteenth century—to seek out and bring to battle the enemy's principal forces. Since all that remained of the French Army was incarcerated in Paris, the Prussian general staff had no choice but to lay siege to the city if they were to obtain a surrender of the country at large.

As the two German armies converged upon Paris, General Phil Sheridan, late of the American Civil War, who was "on tour" with the victorious Prussians, reported seeing "two almost continuous lines of broken bottles along the roadsides all the way down from

Sedan." But except for the looting of French wine cellars, the enemy's progress was orderly and unmarked by vandalism.

On 17 September the investment of Paris began with the Army of the Meuse under the crown prince of Saxony enveloping the northern forts and the Prussian crown prince's third army swinging round the southern side. The Germans moved into their seige positions with the utmost prudence. Their numerical weakness made any sudden thrust to break the line of forts out of the question. They had 122,000 infantry and 24,000 cavalry with which to occupy the fifty-mile perimeter around the Paris fortifications. This allowed for a density of only one infantryman per yard.

After establishing headquarters in the palace of Versailles, the Prussians settled down to maintain a watertight embargo until Paris was starved out. Bismarck had already predicted that "eight days without café au lait would break the Parisian bourgeoisie."

Inside the capital, Trochu was equally cautious. He was too pessimistic about the forces at his disposal to risk any major assault against the besiegers. He reasoned that if the best of the regular army had been so badly mauled by the Prussians, there was little hope for the armed rabble of Paris. His strategy was vaguely that of remaining on the defensive and waiting for the Prussians to pound themselves to death against the forts and bastions of the city.

A few small scale engagements were fought by the French, but the heavy Krupp siege guns soon destroyed their hopes of maintaining any positions in advance of the ring of forts. Throughout the autumn the battle for Paris settled down to sniping, outpost skirmishes and artillery duels. Of the futility of the French attacks, General von Blumenthal, chief of staff to the Prussian crown prince, wrote in his journal: "Our lines are so weakly held that, if the enemy should attack at

Bismarck before Paris.

From left to right: Moltke, King Wilhelm, Prince Frederic and Bismarck. (PIX)

one point with the whole of his force concentrated, we must be beaten back and have our line cut through. Fortunately, he does not understand his business, and wastes his strength striking out blindly in all directions."

While there was a stalemate on the front, a rash of inventiveness broke out among Paris civilians. It became necessary to create a *Comité Scientifique* to weight the flood of schemes for the instantaneous annihilation of the enemy. The manufacture of a musical mitrailleuse was pressed in all seriousness. The weapon would be equipped to play Wagner, Schubert and Mendelssohn. The musical Germans would not be able to resist drawing near to listen, and then a barrage of bullets would mow them down.

A recurring scheme was the use of Greek fire, so effective in the Middle Ages, in modern rockets. It was estimated they could kill one thousand Prussians a minute. And so in five hours the siege would be lifted for want of any more besiegers. The one drawback to the rockets was that Greek fire does not easily catch "dry matter." So it was proposed, as a preliminary, that each Prussian be watered with the help of a fire hose. This being somewhat inconvenient, an inventor came up with a "hot-water rifle."

The greatest danger that confronted Trochu in his conduct of the war was the threat of a revolution inside Paris. To many in the moderate camp, *le spectre rouge* was more to be feared than the Prussians. The agitation against the government carried on by the radical socialist, Blanqui, gave rise to the slogan, "Rather Bismarck than Blanqui."

By the end of September, the National Guard, which numbered 360,000, was split into two components—the "reliable" bourgeois and the proletariat. As the siege progressed the *Garde Nationale* rapidly established itself as the storm center of the Left. The proletarian units became known as the "Red" battalions, the first time in history the label emerged in its modern sense.

The "Red" clubs in Belleville and the Montmartre, which had been closed down under the empire, reopened during the siege. *Garde* leaders and a hotchpotch of revolutionaries tinted with the most burning shades of red, jammed the clubs for the amusement value of orators who made violent, unchecked attacks on the government. The left wing kept demanding a *levée en masse,* that dread upsurge of the whole population in arms. Trochu replied that "purposeless sorties by large masses of undisciplined men were hazardous." He might have quoted Machiavelli's warning: "He who commands the defense of a town will shun arming the citizens tumultuously as he would shun a reef."

Only Karl Marx, from his safe exile in England, viewed the situation with sinister optimism. "However the war may end," he wrote to a friend, "it has given the French proletariat practice in arms, and that is the best guarantee for the future."

In London, Louis Adolphe Thiers, the veteran French politician, stressed the "Red Menace" in Paris as an urgent reason for British intervention. But he was hopelessly thwarted by the queen's Germanic ties. Her son-in-law, Crown Prince Frederick of Prussia, commanded one of the two armies encircling Paris. It was unthinkable that she would sanction sending an armed force against her "beloved Fritz."

Thiers' efforts to solicit aid in Vienna and St. Petersburg were equally fruitless. After Von Moltke's smashing thirty-day victory, Europe stood thoroughly in awe of Prussia. Even if, as the French contended, civilization was for the moment, "a prisoner in Paris," nobody cared to risk going to its rescue.

France has always been said to embody the social instinct, and unquestionably, during the siege the

Parisians suffered most acutely from their isolation. Bismarck permitted Elihu Washburne, the American minister who stayed on in the capital throughout the investment, to receive one copy of *The Times* per week, sent by the United States Legation in London. The proviso attached was that Washburne keep the contents of his weekly newspaper strictly to himself.

All during the siege the minister was bombarded with desperate appeals to divulge his news. A Paris journal pleaded: "We gave you Lafayette and Rochambeau, in return for which we only ask for one copy of an English paper."

But even when Washburne allowed edited fragments to filter out, the neurotic Parisians complained they were getting only bad news, and the Americans were withholding the accounts of French victories.

Since the Paris press could get no information whatever from the outside, they fell back upon self-eulogy. It was the only way to fill their columns when reports that "La Province" was rising up with the utmost energy, grew stale. One paper complained of the world looking on impassively "at the ruin of a nation which possesses the most exquisite gifts of sociability, the principal jewel of Europe, and the eternal ornament of civilization."

Although the vise tightened daily around Paris, there remained one spectacular way of getting out of the city and that was by balloon. A Frenchman, De Mongolfier, had invented the first "hot-air" balloon in 1738. It was a perilous device in which passengers, while aloft, had to stoke a fire with straw and wood immediately beneath the highly inflammable paper envelope. The French continued to improve their fragile dirigible. Then, during the siege, Mongolfier's invention paid off richly.

When the investment began there were only seven balloons in the city—most of them in disrepair. Symbolically, the *Impérial* was in shreds. But aeronauts worked feverishly with paste-pot and paper to patch them up for flight. On 23 September the *Neptune* was wafted over the heads of the astonished Prussians. After a three-hour flight it landed safely beyond the enemy lines with 125 kilograms of government messages. Thereafter, a regular Balloon Post—the capital's sole link with the provinces—was established.

The balloons were constructed of varnished cotton and filled with highly explosive coal-gas which a bullet from a Prussian sharp-shooter could turn into a ball of flame. Their motion was largely uncontrollable. In inexperienced hands they might shoot up suddenly to 6000 feet—then fall back almost to ground level, so it was little short of miraculous how many got through the embargo. The balloonists, huddled in open wicker baskets with no protection from the elements, suffered agonizingly in the severe winter. And since the winds blew them all over France, and beyond, they seldom had the remotest idea where they were landing.

At best, the balloon lift only worked one way. Nobody ever figured out how to make the return journey. So it fell to the humble carrier-pigeon to break the blockade in reverse. The success of the pigeon-post was due to the inventions of Dragon, a Parisian expert in microphotography. He managed to get himself flown to Tours after the investment, and there he set up the first microphotographic unit ever to be employed in war. Government dispatches in Tours were reduced to a minute size, printed on feathery collodian membranes, then rolled into a pellicle so that one pigeon could carry up to 40,000 dispatches, equivalent to the contents of a book. On reaching Paris, the dispatches were projected by magic lantern and transcribed by a staff of clerks. Sometimes one pigeon-load would require a week to decipher.

But for the pigeons, as for the balloonists, casualties

were high. Of the 302 birds sent off in the course of the siege, 59 reached Paris. The rest were either killed by birds of prey—the enemy deliberately sent up falcons to attack them—or they succumbed to cold and hunger. Quite a few of the gallant postmen ended up in Prussian pies.

On 8 December, Goncourt noted in his journal, "People are talking only of what they eat, what they can eat and what there is to eat." With the approach of Christmas, the food stores collected for the duration of the siege had run out. Milk, butter, cheese and eggs were extinct. There were no fresh vegetables except an occasional frost-bitten cauliflower or potato which scavengers grubbed up in no-man's land. Even the vast herds which filled the Bois in September had vanished. Boldly, a new sign made its appearance: "Feline and Canine Butchers." The populace, shocked at first, soon grew callous to the sight of the dog-and-cat butchers pushing carts through the streets from which emanated doleful barks and miaws.

Labouchere, the *Daily News* correspondent, mentioned casually in a letter home, "I had a slice of spaniel the other day." He also reported that a Parisian was fattening up a huge cat which he intended to serve up on Christmas, roasted, and "surrounded with mice like sausages."

The holiday display in one jeweler's window on the Rue de la Paix, was "a dead rabbit, flanked by a plate of minnows and three tiny sparrows; while higher up half a dozen's hen's eggs were arranged in a circlet like a necklace of pearls."

As a sign of the times, a young singer at a concert, received, along with the applause, not a bouquet—but a piece of cheese. Horsemeat, which started out as provender for the poor, became very much a la mode during the siege. Gourmands even maintained the light-greys had a much finer flavour than the blacks. Famous

Napoleon III during his imprisonment at Wilhelmshohe Castle. (PIX)

Enrollment of French volunteers.

LA PATRIE EST EN DANGE

Bismarck leading the victorious German troops beneath the Arc de Triomphe, March 1, 1871. (PIX)

Proclamation of the German Empire at Versailles.

Soldiers and civilians at a victory dance in Berlin. (PIX)

A contemporary photograph of the triumphal entry into Berlin in June, 1871. (PIX)

race-horses ended up in casseroles. Even the imperial stables were not exempt. The two superb trotters presented to Louis-Napoleon by the Tsar at the time of the Great Exhibition, and valued at 56,000 francs, were sold to a butcher for 800, and turned into "equine sausage."

As time passed, even the zoos had to surrender their inmates. The lions and tigers were spared because of the danger involved in killing them. And hungry as the Parisians were, they bypassed the monkeys on account of Darwin. The hippopotamus from the Jardin des Plantes was saved by the scales. No butcher was rich enough to afford his price by the live pound–80,000 francs–so he waddled back to his cage. Everything else was eaten.

From December on, rats were regularly sold in the butcher shops. A discriminating taste had even developed to the point where there was a price difference between "brewery and sewer rats." But contrary to legend, few were actually eaten during the siege. Fear of the diseases they supposedly carried, acted as a taboo. Besides, so many sauces were required to make them palatable they were mainly a rich man's dish, as when the Jockey Club featured its famous *salmi de rats* and "rat pie." Proletarian Belleville and the Montmartre could never afford such delicacies. According to all reports, one comfort remained to the besieged. Even when Paris was approaching her last rat, the alcohol never ran out.

On 5 January the war entered a new phase. The German bombardment of Paris proper began, the shells falling at a rate of between three and four hundred a day. The move won immediate support abroad for the trapped Parisians. An outcry went up in the foreign press that the Prussians had not even given notice before bombarding a city full of defenseless people. All the principal nations made diplomatic protests.

But from a military standpoint the bombardment was a failure. Aside from the ghastly mutilation of those unlucky enough to be struck by shells, there were few deaths. Monstrous as Krupp's mortars were by nineteenth century standards, they were still inadequate to the task. The Paris houses were built of such solid blocks of stone they could only be destroyed piecemeal. One bomb simply displaced one stone. It was reckoned that in the three weeks the bombardment of Paris lasted, only 97 people were killed and 278 wounded; 1,400 buildings were damaged. This cost the Prussians 12,000 shells, as well as several hundred gunners lost to French counter-battery fire.

The Parisians were distraught that a Prussian shell had landed on the priceless collection of orchids under glass in the Jardin des Plantes. The treasures of the Louvre were safe, having been shipped off to Brest. But the populace soon turned the menace into a diversion going out every night to watch the shelling, which the Germans began punctually at 10 p.m.

In the end, it was neither hunger nor the Prussian bombardment which brought Paris to the breaking-point, but fear of rebellion. As General Ducrot, the regular army commander, said later: "One was constantly obliged to face two enemies: one which, night and day tightened his ring of fire and steel, the other which at every instant was awaiting the moment to hurl itself upon the Hotel de Ville."

As Paris hardened into two irreconcilable camps, the government, rather than wage a war on two fronts, considered it imperative to obtain an armistice with the least delay. On 27 January, after 130 days, the siege was over. According to the terms of the armistice, the army was to surrender its arms and its colors, but the officers would be left their swords. Paris would pay a war indemnity of two hundred million francs, surrender the perimeter forts to the Prussians, and throw the rampart guns into the moats, but no Prussian troops would enter Paris for the duration of the armistice, which was to last until 19 February. During this time an assembly was to be elected at Bordeaux to discuss the terms of a definitive peace treaty. As a concession to French pride, Paris was allowed to fire the last shot of the siege. Then the guns fell silent.

Immediately after the surrender, the kaiser instructed that six million army rations be sent into Paris. The countryside, being itself devastated, and its communications disrupted, could do little to relieve the starving city. The principal revictualing was done by Britain and America. Gladstone's government requisitioned Navy ships loaded with rations for dispatch to French ports. The Lord Mayor's Relief Fund was inundated with donations. Some $2,000,000 worth of food was sent from the United States.

As provisions began to reach Paris, France went to the polls to elect a new government which would be responsible for the peace terms. The vast majority of seats were won by deputies with conservative, Catholic, and rural sympathies. Out of 768 seats, over 400 went to monarchists. The behaviour of the Reds in Paris during the siege had greatly influenced the provincial swing. Victor Hugo had declaimed, "O City, you will make history kneel down before you!" History might, but not the provinces.

Paris, enraged at coming out of the election with only forty-three seats, called the assembly, "the country bumpkins."

Adolphe Thiers, a consummate politician with aristocratic tastes and associations, was elected president. A realist above everything else, he was determined to conclude "peace at almost any price." A *Daily News* correspondent, referring to the peace terms, remarked that "If France is ruined, she is at least sure to get from M. Thiers a first class funeral."

Still, peace negotiations at Versailles dragged on for six days. Bismarck, losing patience, declared that unless the treaty was immediately concluded, the German forces would resume hostilities against "whatever they could find to fight." That night, 26 February, the treaty was signed. Thiers, on his way back to Paris, broke down and wept in his carriage. France lost Alsace and most of Lorraine—two of her most valuable provinces—as well as the fortress cities of Metz and Strasbourg. She was required to pay an unprecedented war indemnity of six milliard francs—although it was later reduced to five milliards—and until it was paid in full she had to submit to partial occupation.

Thiers agreed to allow the Germans to make a triumphal march through Paris and occupy the city for two days. Although the capital was convulsed with rage at this humiliation, there were no untoward incidents. The march began at 8 a.m. on 1 March, when troopers of the Fourteenth Prussian Hussars rode up the Etoile, jumped their horses over the chains, and other obstructions the Parisians had placed around the Arc de Triomphe, and led the way insouciantly through the sacred edifice.

At Longchamps the 30,000 troops picked for the triumphal entry, passed in review before the new emperor of Germany. As the men who had fought at Woerth, Gravelotte, Orleans, and from Sedan to Paris, goose-stepped past, Archibald Forbes, the *Daily News* correspondent with the German forces, was overcome with a sense of history. When the procession was moving off, he recorded a touching encounter. "The Kaiser turned his horse and met his son face to face. Hand went out to hand, and the grip was given of love and mutual appreciation." Behind them followed what looked to Forbes like "half the Almanack de Goth."

The splendid martial display evoked a far different response from the populace. The last German had no sooner withdrawn through the Arc de Triomphe than the Parisians began scrubbing the streets the enemy's feet had trodden with Condy's Fluid. While all over the city immense bonfires were lighted to purify the tainted pavement and even the air which the conquerors had breathed.

A Scrap of Paper

by Angela Stuart

On June of 1914, Brussels settled down as usual for its long summer siesta. The social season ended in June with the queen's garden party. After that, the nobility went to their chateaux in the country or off to various watering places for the cure. Even if they remained in town they closed their houses. The Quartier Leopold, sacred to the aristocracy and which lies west of the boulevards of the "upper town," was deserted. All the stately old mansions with their grey or white facades had heavy shutters up at the windows. Only servants went in and out of the great doors. Sometimes an ancient fiacre rattled over the uneven cobblestones, but there were no other signs of life.

Like everything else in the Quartier Leopold, the American Legation on the corner of the rue Belliard and the rue de Treves was battened down, while the Minister, Brand Whitlock, and his family retired to a villa in a charming woods near the capital. The embassy was the smallest possible organization—the minister, secretary, and one clerk—since it was well known that nothing ever happened in Belgium.

On the morning of June 15, Mr. Whitlock, a former mayor of Toledo, was in his study at work on the manuscript of a long-projected novel which was laid in the far-off Ohio town where he had spent his boyhood. He had been looking forward eagerly to this hiatus in official duties, this serene vacuum, in order to get on with his book.

Suddenly the telephone bell rang, in itself a shocking intrusion, it rang so seldom. At the other end, a Belgian servant who had been left at the embassy exclaimed, "*Excellence, le prince heriter d'Autriche a été assassiné á Sarajevo!*"

The minister had never heard of Sarajevo. What it did mean was that he must return to town at once to make a formal call at the Austrian Legation.

Three days later a solemn requiem High Mass was sung for the repose of the soul of the murdered prince in the Church of Saint Jacques sur Caudenberg, impressive with hangings of black velvet embroidered in silver, a black catafalque with the Austrian arms, and a myriad of crackling candles. Brussels' entire diplomatic corps, hurriedly called back from the four corners of Europe, was in attendance. They offered their condolences to their Austrian colleague, and again dispersed. In a week the matter seemed forgotten. No doubt the diplomats would smother the fire that smoldered in the Balkans with their official notes, as they had always done in the past.

But late in July this comfortable assurance was shattered when the Austrian government gave Serbia only forty-eight hours in which to accept eleven conditions,

Edith Cavell.

several of which infringed upon Serbian sovereignty. Even the aged Emperor Franz Joseph, after reading the final draft of the note, had shaken his head, muttering that it was "*sehr harte*"—very harsh. Serbia would reject the conditions if Russia backed her. In that case, existing alliances made it certain that if all parties honored their obligations, a local war would swiftly become general.

In Brussels the diplomatic corps took comfort in Belgium's neutral status. On April 19, 1839, Belgium and Holland had signed a treaty providing that "Belgium will form an independent and perpetually neutral state." On the same date, Prussia, France, Great Britain, Austria, and Russia signed a second treaty by which they jointly became the guarantors of such perpetual neutrality.

But opposed to the treaty and its chivalrous intent was a terrible geographic expediency. Belgium, with its plains and plateaus rich in variegated resources and everywhere intersected by roads and railways, was probably the only region in the world where an army of more than one million men could make a rapid passage. The Belgian fortifications of Liege and Namur were situated exactly on the line of invasion whether from France toward Germany, or from Germany toward France. It was almost a foregone conclusion that whichever of these historic adversaries wanted to strike the first blow *must* cross Belgian territory.

And so, as the contagion of war jitters spread northward, the Belgian government, on July 29, decreed mobilization. Troops would be stationed on the frontiers against all comers. At midnight, the police went about Brussels ringing doorbells, summoning men to the colors. The reserves tumbled out of bed, put on the Belgian uniform—a rough blue tunic, linen pantaloons, and the little *bonnet de police* with a gay tassel hanging down on the forehead—and went off to join their regiments. Belgian carabiniers mounted their bicycles, and even the dog teams were barking with excitement as they pulled the *mitrailleuses* toward the frontier.

The most dreadful things seemed to happen on a Sunday—first on the Sunday of Sarajevo with the assassination of Archduke Franz Ferdinand, and then on Sunday, the second of August, Germany delivered her historic ultimatum to Belgium, in its way a masterpiece of Machiavellian diplomacy. It began:

"Very Confidential—Reliable information has been received by the German Government to the effect that French forces intend to march on the line of the Meuse by Givet and Namur. This information leaves no doubt as to the intention of France to march through Belgium territory against Germany.

"The German Government cannot but fear that Belgium, in spite of the utmost goodwill, will be unable, without assistance, to repel so considerable a French invasion with sufficient prospect of success to afford an adequate guarantee against danger to Germany. It is essential for the self-defense of Germany that she should anticipate any such hostile attack."

The ultimatum concluded with the promise that if Belgium adopted a friendly attitude, Germany was prepared to purchase all necessities for her troops while passing through Belgium, against a cash payment, and to pay an indemnity for any damage that might result.

Original German plans called for the violation of three neutralities—Luxembourg, Belgium, and Holland. But by careful staff work it was pared down to two. The Netherlands was spared to be a source of imports to the landlocked Central Powers. "Holland," as Chief-of-Staff Von Moltke wrote, "must be the windpipe that enables us to breathe."

After the receipt of the German ultimatum, lights burned in the Belgian ministries all night where King Albert presided over a cabinet council. At seven a.m.

on August 3, the time the ultimatum expired, a calm and stately reply was delivered to the German minister. Belgium refused to break her engagements to her Allies and would resist German aggression to the end.

German diplomats and consular officials in Brussels were terribly unstrung by the Belgian stand. From the German Embassy the wail went up, "Oh, the poor fools! Why don't they get out of the way of the steam roller?"

Ultimata were flying thick and fast. On August 4, in the early hours of the morning, German troops crossed the Belgian frontier. Almost immediately the British ambassador in Berlin, Sir Edward Goshen, presented England's ultimatum to the German Chancellor Bethmann-Hollweg. It was a staggering blow to the Hohenzollern camp. Britain was not involved by formal alliance in European quarrels. She was in no way obliged by treaty to go to war, except for the presence of German troops on Belgian soil.

Bethmann was extremely agitated. He told the British ambassador his blood boiled at this hypocritical harping on Belgium, that England was doing an unthinkable thing in making war on "a kindred nation." As a result of "this last terrible step" England would be responsible for all the dreadful events that might follow, and all for just a word—"neutrality"—just for "a scrap of paper."

This dismissal of the treaty of 1839 by which Germany had solemnly guaranteed Belgian neutrality as "a scrap of paper" quickly reverberated round the world. The phrase, in its naked frankness, aroused the man in the street, damaging German prestige in neutral countries, especially America, before the war had even begun.

As Brussels prepared for the invaders, the city was one great moving flag—black, red, and yellow. Most of the shops were closed. Nearly every big hotel turned its dining room into a ward to accommodate the wounded. The guests were required to have meals in their rooms. Big department stores emptied their stocks to outfit hospitals and workrooms. The Red Cross emblem was suddenly as omnipresent as the figure of St. Michael, patron of Brussels, who struggled with the dragon on all lampposts and letterboxes.

Overnight it became highly unfortunate to be blond. The excitable population of Brussels was constantly on the lookout for German spies. The cry *Espion!* went up at the mere sight of a civilian with a blond beard and chubby face. Even Burgomaster Max, Mayor of Brussels, who happened to be fair, was once chased several blocks before the mistake became apparent.

The *Bruxellois* had a reputation for unquenchable gaiety on the eve of crisis—and there had been many in their troubled history. On the night of June 15, 1815, Wellington and his officers attended a gala ball in Brussels given by the duchess of Richmond. "Everyone" was there. Only when the roar of French cannon became unmistakable above the violins did Wellington's commanders buckle on their swords and rush from the ballroom to Quatre-Bras on the road to Waterloo, where Napoleon had stolen a 24 hours' march on his opponents. But in August of 1914 there were no balls. It was a thoroughly chastened city which constantly awaited news from *Là-bas* where the tiny Belgian forces held the frontier forts.

Liege, with its circle of subterranean forts, commanded the close defile through which General Von Kluck's First Army of 320,000 had to pass in order to deploy on the Belgian plain. In a proclamation to the defenders of Liege, King Albert cited Caesar's phrase, known to schoolboys the world over: "*Horum omnium fortissimi sunt Belgae.*" "Of all the peoples of Gaul, the Belgians are the bravest." The heroic resistance of the garrisons astonished everyone. Men meeting in the streets of Brussels shook hands and exclaimed ecstatically, "*Les forts tiennent toujours!*" The French Republic conferred the Legion of Honor on the city of Liege.

It was a contest between David and Goliath in which Germany lost 42,000 men—more than the total strength of the opposing Belgian divisions. Four thousand Belgians stationed within the ring of forts at Liege immobilized 100,000 Germans for ten days and so permitted a strategic reshuffling of the French armies. But the Germans had to break through at any cost. They brought up heavy guns of a caliber so far unknown, and on August 16, the last forts were taken.

The Belgians fell back all along the line. The general staff and what was left of the army retreated to fortified Antwerp. As Burgomaster Max said pathetically, "We must save a remnant of our army, there is no way to get another." The royal family and the Belgian government also withdrew to the greater safety of the seacoast city and port of Antwerp.

Tilly, a 16th-century German general, once said, "After all, you can't put an army in a sack and carry it across a country." The living proof of his words, embodied in General Von Kluck's First Army, entered Brussels August 20. Business was suspended and there were posters everywhere with the proclamation of the burgomaster urging his people to refrain from hostile acts. Sullen and depressed crowds lined the boulevards for the spectacle of the triumphant entry. The Germans had already marked the route into the city with arrows painted on boards fixed to trees.

First came the *Garde Ulamen,* black and white pennants fluttering from their lances. As they poured down a hill into the lower town, the silence was uncanny. Not an order was shouted nor a word spoken among the officers or men. All orders and signals were given by whistles and signs.

Then came the infantry, without fife, drums, or flags—endless green-grey columns in heavy marching order. Everything was grey, even their helmets and the buttons on their uniforms were covered with grey cloth, while the dust from the thousands of tramping feet made everything greyer still.

No contingency had been overlooked. The horses, shod for a campaign in the country, did a lot of slipping on the smooth cobblestones. But the instant a horse went down a soldier was ready with a coarse cloth to go under his head and another to place under his forefeet, so he would have some grip when he tried to get up and would not hurt himself slipping and pawing at the cobbles.

Many of the officers' faces were so disfigured with dueling scars they resembled Kaffir warriors. All were superbly equipped, wearing upon their chests great electric searchlights attached to batteries in saddlebags for use on the march to read signposts and study maps. Kitchens on wheels, each drawn by four horses, accompanied the main body of troops, stoves lighted and smoke pouring from the chimneys as cooks prepared the evening meal. Here and there large motor trucks were fitted out as cobblers' shops, each with a dozen cobblers pounding away at boots which were passed up to them by the marching soldiers. While waiting for repairs to be made, the troops rode on the wide running-board of the truck.

In sheer efficiency it was the most remarkable army the world had ever known. But at last, the Belgians—becoming surfeited with the spectacle—went home. The lamps were lighted on the boulevards in a dust dense as fog, and still the grey hordes kept filing by like grey ghosts in a grey twilight.

On the morning of August 21, the citizens of Brussels, who numbered around 700,000, awoke to find that liberty had evaporated in the night. Their beloved city was covered with *affiches*—great white placards printed in French and German, making known the will of their conquerors. It was *verboten* to leave the city, to possess a firearm or inflammable oil, to hoard food, to hum, sing, or whistle the *Marseillaise* or the *Brabanconne* (the national anthem of Belgium), to wear patriotic insignia, to disseminate false information injurious to the morale of the German troops—all reports of Allied gains automatically falling into the category of "false information."

The list would grow from day to day and week to week until it was even *verboten* for Belgian pigeons to fly.

There were no trains or trams, horses, taxies, or automobiles—except those in which German officers traveled about town like cyclones, a soldier on the box with a rifle across his knees. All communication by telephone, telegraph, or by postal service had been cut off. Even newspapers were banned.

The heart of Brussels was the Grand' Place, often considered the most beautiful square in Europe. Here were the ancient guild houses, and the fifteenth-century Hotel de Ville, its tapering spire topped by a golden St. Michael standing triumphant over a slain dragon. The square had changed little since the morning when some man dashed in to relate the news of the discovery of America.

It was in the Grand' Place that the Germans established army headquarters. Where there had been flower stalls heaped with azaleas, carnations, and gladioli under brilliant parasol-like awnings, there were stacks of artillery. In the center were camp kitchens. The courtyard of the Hotel de Ville, where the burgomaster received visiting royalty, had been turned into a stable. Beer bottles were everywhere. It was noticed that breweries were always scrupulously respected by the

Germans. While every other form of transport had vanished from the streets of Brussels, the long beer wagons could still be seen, drawn by teams of superb *Brabanconne* horses.

Most of the diplomatic corps had left the capital. Only two important legations remained, the American and the Spanish. It was believed by the ministers that the presence of diplomatic representatives of neutral powers would act as a restraint upon the Germans. At least there was no other. At the beginning of the occupation, the American diplomats were the pampered pets of both sides. The German troops cheered whenever a legation car, flying its tiny American flag on the engine, nosed its way through their ranks; Belgians on the street, at sight of the flag, always uncovered and loudly cried, *"Vive l'Amerique!"*

And through it all everyone remarked about the weather. Ordinarily skies were leaden and it rained as often as in Scotland. But in August of 1914, day followed day filled to the brim with brilliant sunlight. "Of all the havoc of this year," as Goethe once wrote in his journal, "Nature in her usual way took not the slightest notice."

As months passed and German oppression increased, Belgian resistance kept pace with it. The resistance took many forms. Often it was occult, an indefinable something in the air, as when the Belgians walked about the city shoulder to shoulder with their foes, but never appeared to see them. The most daring affront of all to the conquerors was the loyalist organization which formed near the French border in the autumn of 1914. As the first German units entered Belgium, commanders ordered that a white cross be chaulked on the gates of certain chateaux. To the troops who followed, it meant *"Nicht Plunderen"*—"Don't pillage." However, in the case of the magnificent Chateau de Bellignies, surrounded by a densely wooded park of 30,000 acres, the white cross backfired upon the invaders.

The chateau belonged to the De Croys, one of the oldest families of the Belgian nobility with branches throughout Europe. It was practically empty except for the Princess Marie de Croy and her brother, Prince Reginald, who was entrusted by the absentee Belgian government with various important commissions. Other members of the family were away, serving with the armies of both sides.

When word reached the princess that hundreds of Allied soldiers—who had been separated from their regiments during the battles of Dinant, Namur, and Mons—were hiding out in the neighborhood, she immediately made plans to receive them at the chateau. Taking advantage of the fact that the entire De Croy estate was immune from German search parties, she organized a group of Belgians of all classes—professional men, shopkeepers, peasants—to assist the Allied fugitives to reach the Chateau de Bellignies. The downstairs rooms with their priceless pictures and bibelots became a dressing station where the Princess de Croy, together with a few elderly retainers, gave first aid to the wounded and those suffering from severe mental shock. All the men were near starvation. Temporary shelter was provided for the fugitives in the cottages of the woodsmen who lived in the forested park.

The risks involved in the operation were very great. The Germans were continually combing the area for stragglers whom they shot on sight. At night motor patrols came with great searchlights and played them over the fields. The lights verged on, but did not penetrate, the wooded fastness surrounding the chateau, where hundreds of Allied troops were recuperating. The De Croys were too well connected with the German aristocracy to arouse the least suspicion.

But as winter approached and more and more fugitives found their way to the chateau, food shortages became acute. It was necessary to send the soldiers north to a receiving station in Brussels where they might be sheltered for a few days until contact could be made with guides who would conduct them to the border. Once in neutral Holland they could return to their own lines.

It was this last phase of the rescue work that was the most nerve-racking. Reliable guides were hard to find. Most of the fugitives were English, with a sprightly walk that made it difficult to conceal their nationality. Once at the frontier, a German sentry could sometimes be bribed to look the other way, but as surveillance was tightened the bribes became exorbitant. Besides, the Dutch border was strung with barbed wire entanglements, and high fences had been erected whose wires were charged with electricity. Scores of men lost their lives within a few yards of liberty, shot down by sentries or electrocuted.

While the De Croys were searching for a receiving agent, they heard rumors of an English nurse, the directress of the training school in Brussels, who had already given assistance to two stranded British officers. Her name was Edith Cavell.

As the daughter of a Church of England clergyman, Miss Cavell had been brought up in the bare, plain living of a remote country vicarage. Her father had a stern puritanical sense of duty, and from earliest childhood she had made the rounds with her parents, giving aid to the poor and the sick.

There was an unwritten law in the Cavell family that whenever they had a hot roast they must share it with six others less fortunate than themselves. Six basins with covers would be brought to the table into which Reverend Cavell placed hot food to be taken by the children to six needy villagers. By the time the deliveries were made and the children got back to the table, their own food was long since cold.

When Edith was growing up, a cousin once asked her what she wanted to do in life. Her reply, as he remembered it, foreshadowed her whole future. "I don't know. I only know it must be something for people. They are, most of them, so helpless, so hurt, and so unhappy."

Her opportunity for a life of service came in 1907 when she was chosen by the foremost doctors of Brussels to act as matron of the first nurses' training school to be opened in Belgium. She had been thoroughly schooled in the great modern hospitals in the slums of London.

When she arrived in Brussels nursing conditions were no further advanced than in England in 1860, before Florence Nightingale established training schools. There wasn't one professionally trained nurse in the whole of Belgium. The care of the sick was largely in the hands of nuns, and while they were devoted to their patients, they were untrained in modern methods and imbued with the medieval routine of the convent. There were things they would not, or could not, do. If patients wanted to be washed, they had to do it themselves or bribe a servant to render the service for them. Whenever a doctor gave a treatment, he had to stop and make up the bed afterwards. The need for the professionally conscious nurse was especially acute in surgery cases with their high mortality rate.

Nevertheless, before Miss Cavell could make any headway, she had to break down the intense disapprobation in which nursing was held in Belgium. The lay-nurse was usually unscrupulous, illiterate, and addicted to the bottle besides—much the same type as Dickens immortalized in "Sairey Gamp" whose professional point of view was summed up in a conversation with a fellow nurse. "Wishin' you lots of sickness, my darlin' creeture and good places. And may our next meetin' be at a large family's, where they all takes it reg'lar, one from another, turn and turn about."

The training school, *L'Ecole Belge d'Infirmières Diplomés,* opened in September of 1907. It was a block of four connecting houses on the rue de la Culture, flush with the street, and in the back were charming little gardens. After prolonged interviews Miss Cavell induced five young women from respectable families, and with moral standards far removed from "Sairey Gamp," to undertake the course.

At first the English directress had to shoulder nearly all the burdens—the supervision of the household, lectures to the probationers, as well as the care of the sick in the infirmary attached to the school. She was a stern disciplinarian and was quite generally regarded by the Belgians, with their Latin temperament, as a puritan. Being themselves so gay and pleasure loving, they would never understand her uncompromising sense of duty and her serious driving will. Her only leisure time was a few minutes over a cup of tea at four o'clock when she unbent a little in her implacable reserve. There were no days off, but once a year there was a month's holiday in England at the vicarage or the seashore.

Miss Cavell befriended all stray dogs, and one great, long-haired mongrel named Jack was entrenched in the rue de la Culture despite the objections of many Belgians who did not think a nursing school the place for a dog. Besides, they never became sentimental over dogs the way the English did. But Jack remained and always accompanied his mistress when she walked from the school to St. Giles hospital where she was matron. Passers-by would glance curiously at the pair—the small, serious, grey-eyed nurse in a long, dark blue cape over a dark blue uniform and the big, shaggy mongrel trotting at her side.

Belgium was slow to accept the idea of the professionally trained nurse. But five years after its establishment, the school on the rue de la Culture provided the nursing for three hospitals, three private clinics, 24 common schools, and 13 kindergartens in Brussels. Most remarkable of all, when war broke out two years later nursing facilities were available to meet the crisis.

When Prince De Croy called upon Edith Cavell to ask that she become the receiving agent for fugitive soldiers in Brussels, he was impressed by the location of the school, which was in a suburb away from the heavily guarded main thoroughfares. Nor was Miss Cavell—quiet, reserved, inconspicuous—likely to arouse the suspicion of the Germans.

For her own part, she consented to take on the grave responsibility because it involved so many "English *soldats*" whom the Belgians idolized as their deliverers and were risking their lives to protect. But she refused to incriminate anyone under her supervision. From the start she carried the burden alone, managing everything with such quiet efficiency not even the student nurses knew that Allied soldiers were hiding in their midst.

By summer of 1915, the Germans had given up all hope of "a short, old-fashioned war." The capital was sunk in a torpor of stagnation. "Every day is like every other in its cussedness," Hugh Gibson, secretary of the American Legation, wrote in his journal. Wherever one looked, there was the *affiche* and the Prussian helmet, and at all hours, the hoarse shouts, *"Achtung!"*—the order to a squad to break into the goosestep.

As July 21, the Belgian national holiday, approached, there was a small flurry of excitement. The Germans, knowing full well the Belgian passion for celebrations, placarded the walls of Brussels with *affiches* rigorously prohibiting any demonstration whatsoever, including the wearing of ribbons or patriotic insignia. All the same, there was a celebration.

Word was passed among the inhabitants that since the nation was in mourning, its anniversary would be observed, not with rejoicing, but with a solemn display of grief. Everything closed—shops, banks, hotels, with the exception of those taken over by the Germans. All houses had blinds drawn and shutters up. On the streets vendors sold combinations of red and yellow flowers to passers-by, and these against the formal black coats the bourgeois were wearing made up the forbidden national colors.

In due time the Germans got out another *affiche* forbidding the people to make demonstrations or in any way observe August 4, the sinister anniversary of the beginning of the war between Belgium and Germany. The penalty for disobedience was exile for five years in Germany and ten thousand marks.

The fourth of August, 1915, passed quietly enough, but all over the city men wore as *boutonnières* little scraps of paper, recalling the famous phrase by which Bethmann-Hollweg had characterized the treaty which Germany had violated a year before.

Despite the omnipresence of German spies—there were 6000 in the capital alone—the little clandestine newspaper, *La Libre Belgique,* continued to make its appearance. No one knew who edited it or by whom it was published. It was a four-page sheet which said anything it liked about the "Occupant." It also published news that was barred from the censored German press. It was, according to its own announcement, "A Bulletin of Patriotic Propaganda, irregularly regular" in appearance. The price of a number was "elastic, from zero to infinity." Its telegraph address was "Kommandantur, Brussels," the German police headquarters.

It would turn up mysteriously in people's letterboxes, and then it would come no more. After a while the distribution would be renewed. But it never failed to reach the governor-general of Belgium, Baron von Bissing, despite the fact that his offices were as heavily guarded as the vaults of the Bank of England. Sometimes it was delivered by an orderly, buried in a bundle of dispatches, or with letters from Germany. Again it would come flying through the window, or it would simply appear from nowhere and be lying on the governor-general's desk when he arrived in the morning.

Enraged by such audacity, the Germans offered large rewards for information that would lead to the suppression of the valiant little paper, but neither the editor nor printer of *La Libre Belgique* was ever discovered.

Autumn came early in 1915 with bitter fog and drizzling rain. As signs of the season, roasted chestnuts were exposed on window ledges around the Grand' Place, and women sold fresh walnuts from carts. Despite the cold the German band played regularly in front of the Bourse. And German officers, who always had to be shooting something, took their fowling pieces and went off to hunt in the beautiful Foret de Soignes.

In September, the American Legation, which was entrusted with the protection of British interests in Belgium, learned that the nurse, Edith Cavell, had been arrested by the Germans for *trahison de guerre* and was confined in the military prison of St. Giles. At the same time, the Princess Marie de Croy and 35 other Belgians belonging to the loyalist organization had been incarcerated in the prison to await trial. The Prince De Croy, absent on a government mission, had not been captured.

Brand Whitlock immediately pressed Baron von der Lancken, political governor of Belgium, for a report on the Cavell case, and permission to provide for her defense. But there was very little information even a neutral legation could get from the Germans concerning political prisoners. As Cicero said, "The law is silent during war."

Alongside a German courtmartial, a tribunal during the French Revolution was soft and sentimental. The accused had no rights. The lawyer for the defense could not see his client before the trial began, and could not speak to the accused in court. Often he did not know what the accusation was until the trial began, as there were no written charges.

At eight o'clock on the evening of October 11, two terrified white-faced nurses appeared at the American Embassy. They said they had just learned that the court had condemned Miss Cavell to death, that the judgment had been read to her in the cell of the prison at four-thirty that afternoon, and that the Germans were going to shoot her that night at two o'clock.

The minister could not believe it. It was too preposterous. All the same, being seriously ill himself, he immediately sent Secretary Hugh Gibson, armed with formal requests for a stay of execution, to the German Ministry for Foreign Affairs. Gibson was accompanied by Maitre de Leval, a Belgian acting as legal advisor to the American Legation, and the Spanish minister, the Marquis de Villalobar.

They reached the ministry in the pouring rain and found it pitch dark. They rang and rang, and finally a concierge answered who knew nothing. After another long wait, a German orderly appeared who said that His Excellence, Baron von der Lancken, was at the theatre. Being given to understand the presence of the governor was urgently needed, the orderly consented to go off with the chauffeur in the American Legation motor in search of him.

Gibson, Villalobar, and De Leval were shown into the Louis XVI yellow salon of the ministry—a gay, frivolous little room oddly at variance with the mood of their errand. It was an interesting trio who had come at the eleventh hour to plead for the life of an English nurse. Hugh Gibson, in his early thirties, known as "the stormy petrol" of the American State Department; the eminent jurist, De Leval, kind and bespectacled; and the Marquis de Villalobar, the most colorful and mysterious figure on the Belgian scene.

When the marquis first arrived in Brussels, there was a flurry of excitement in the diplomatic corps. Not only was he remarkably handsome, and a connoisseur of all the arts, but he was descended from the line of the Dukes of Alba. His aloofness proved a dreadful disappointment.

Once at a reception, a lady sought him out to talk about Spain. While traveling in Castile as a young girl, she had heard that a child, perfectly normal in other respects, but entirely without legs, had been born to a noble family. "Whatever became of the monster?" she asked.

"Madame," replied Villalobar, with his usual suavity, "I am that monster."

The Empress Eugenie, herself of Spanish birth, had sent the unfortunate young Villalobar to a famous English doctor who devised an intricate contrivance by which he learned to walk without arousing too much suspicion. While he had shunned the brilliant social life of the diplomatic corps in Brussels, once the Germans arrived he became immediately available for any act of mercy, and worked unceasingly to alleviate the sufferings of the Belgians.

The Baron von der Lancken returned to the ministry at midnight, having waited to the very end of the performance. Tall and distinguished in his silver helmet and pale blue military cape lined in scarlet, he seemed an impersonation of Lohengrin. But his mood was cold and uncompromising. There was no doubt he resented this meddling on the part of neutrals, especially the not-so-neutral Americans.

His callers explained their mission, and immediately Lancken threw up his hands. "Impossible! Orders are never executed with such precipitation, especially where a woman is concerned." In any event the government offices were closed and nothing could be done. He suggested that they all go home "reasonably," sleep quietly, and come back in the morning to talk about the case. They protested that in the morning there would be no case, and urged him to call the prison to find out the facts.

Lancken left the room, and after a few minutes returned, looking embarrassed. "You are right, gentlemen. I have learned by telephone that Miss Cavell has been condemned and that she will be shot tonight."

Then the group sat down, and for an hour and a half the diplomats presented with all the earnestness at their command the plea for clemency. They pointed out that the sentence of death had heretofore been imposed only for cases of espionage, and that Miss Cavell was not even accused by the German authorities of anything so serious. Besides, since the beginning of the war, as the directress of a nursing home, she had cared for large numbers of German soldiers in a way that should make her life sacred to them. They tried to impress upon Lancken the horror of shooting a woman, no matter what her offense, and the frightful effect that such an execution would have throughout the civilized world.

Contemptuously, he replied that on the contrary he was confident that the effect would be excellent. It would serve as a warning. After all, at the courtmartial Miss Cavell, far from denying her guilt, had even furnished additional proof. When asked by the prosecution if she had helped twenty Allied soldiers to escape, she had answered, "Yes, more than twenty, two hundred."

In desperation, Villalobar dragged the Baron into another room to talk to him man-to-man as he could not in front of the others. The Spaniard's voice could be heard passionately imploring, "You can't do this thing! It's idiotic! You'll have another Louvain, another Lusitania . . ."

But it was all futile. Matters had gone too far, according to Lancken. There was no chance for clemency. "Not even the Emperor himself could intervene." (The kaiser took exception to this statement, which was entirely false. He could have stopped the execution at any moment.)

On the night of October 11, a Church of England clergyman was finally allowed to visit Edith Cavell in her cell. She gave him the letters she had written, including the one to her nurses citing the achievements of the school and urging them to persevere in their devotion to duty. It concluded, "Perhaps, sometimes, I have been too severe, but never voluntarily unjust, and I loved you all much more than you thought."

After partaking of Holy Communion she told the minister, "I have nothing to regret. If I had it to do over again, I would do just as I did. Everyone has been so kind to me here in prison, and I have been so grateful for these eight weeks of rest . . . I know now that patriotism is not enough. I must have no hatred and no bitterness toward anyone."

She was taken out and shot before daybreak.

The same courtmartial which had imposed the death penalty upon Edith Cavell—principally, it was believed, because she was English, and German hatred of Britain had reached its zenith—sentenced Princess Marie de Croy to ten years at hard labor in Germany. Her case was immediately appealed to Berlin. King Alfonso of Spain intervened personally in her behalf, as well as members of the De Croy family in Germany. The kaiser granted the princess a full pardon.

But never had the Germans reckoned on the furor which followed the summary execution of *Die* Cavell, as they contemptuously called the English nurse. Neutral opinion was summed up by an article in the *Amsterdam Telegraf*. "We wrote once in this journal, 'Holland is incapable of shuddering anymore.' We were wrong. The death penalty on a brave woman has caused the whole of this country to freeze with horror." In the words of Talleyrand, "It was worse than a crime, it was a blunder."

But there was another aftermath. News reached Brussels that all along the Western front when British regiments charged over the top of the trenches, they had a new cry—"For Miss Cavell!"

The Guns of Verdun

by Angela Stuart

The Crown Prince Wilhelm, commander of the German Fifth Army in the Verdun sector, liked to take a short stroll after dinner accompanied only by his two whippets. Meals were so plain at army headquarters in a farmhouse in the village of Stenay-sur-Meuse, at the beginning of this second year of the war, as to call for very little walking off. The usual menu, pea soup and sausages-fruit, differed little from an infantry mess. But the atmosphere behind the German lines, on a night in mid-January, 1916, was too charged with excitement for His Imperial Highness to linger with his staff at the candlelit dinner for wine, cigars, and the usual prognostications of an early victory for the Central Powers. He could see little or nothing from the environs of the farmhouse. His adversary, Verdun, the strongest fortress in France, situated along the heights of the right bank of the Meuse, as well as the intervening heavily wooded foothills, was blotted out by one of the heaviest mists of the year. The crown prince, his tall, excessively thin figure emphasized by the long *feldgrau* overcoat, and his equally lean hounds moved easily through the blanket of fog as he searched for some rifts of visibility in which to train his binoculars. It would have seemed the Wagnerian *Nibelungs,* or Beings of the Mist, had taken the defense of Verdun into their own hands. Certainly the fortress would need superhuman help if it were to hold out against the buildup of German arms for the first major assault of the Fifth Army.

By the end of 1915 hostilities on all fronts had reached a stalemate. The conflict the kaiser had predicted would be over "before the leaves fall"—the German timetable had allowed just forty days for Von Kluck's First Army to dash through Belgium and by means of a right wing encirclement deliver a knockout blow to France—had now settled down to a dreary war of attrition.

The strategy of encircling the enemy and squeezing him to death, upon which Germany's hopes of a quick and decisive victory had been based, was known as the Schlieffen Plan. It was devised by a brilliant former chief of the general staff, Count Alfred von Schlieffen, in accordance with the fact that frontal attacks, or breast-to-breast encounters with the enemy, were anathema to the German temperament.

To start with, the odds were considerably in favor of the success of the Schlieffen Plan. Not only were Germany's preparations solid and methodical—it was known at OHL, supreme headquarters in Berlin, the exact second in which a certain troop train would pass over a designated bridge—but the Belgian invasion took France almost completely by surprise.

The French-Belgian frontier was largely undefended

while France pursued her ancient thirst for *revanche* in an Alsace-Lorraine offensive. As a result, the Germans, deploying twice as many troops as they had been credited with, made their advance through Belgium at a terrific rate—the infantry averaging thirty miles a day. If the Schlieffen Plan failed in the end, it was not for want of daring and all-out effort, but because the speed required for its execution took no account of the limits of human endurance. Nor could the supply lines keep up with the race. So that in the last stages of the advance into French territory, whole companies of half-starved German infantry could be seen marching along the dusty roads while sound asleep.

France had also entered the war with a plan—the famous Plan XVII. Like the Schlieffen Plan, by the end of 1915 it, too, was discarded. But for widely different reasons. The essence of Plan XVII was that sufficient will power, or *élan vital,* could make an army invulnerable. In 1914, officers from St. Cyr went into battle wearing white-plumed shakos and white gloves. In the first months they did not carry rifles but led their troops brandishing canes—and as a consequence they were picked off by the hundreds.

French Field Regulations had calculated that in a dash of twenty seconds the infantry would have time to shoulder guns, take aim, and fire. But the Germans, with machine guns, needed only eight seconds to fire, not twenty. It was the factor of firepower against the sabre, lance, and bayonet. And the toll for France was heavy. As 1916 dawned, she had lost the Lorraine iron basin to the Germans along with eighty percent of her iron ore for the duration. Fifty percent of her officers were dead. Whereas she had started out with the ringing cry, *'Offensive à outrance!"*—"Offensive to the limit!"—the order was now being dinned into every French regiment, "Fight in retreat! Fight in retreat!"

On the eve of Verdun, the war on the Western

front was transfixed along a line of trenches from Switzerland to the North Sea. When Joffre, commander-in-chief of the Allied armies, was questioned as to the nature of his strategy, he had announced: *"Je les grignotte."* "I am nibbling them." But the nibbling process hadn't done much more than wear down the teeth of the French forces. The Germans were formidable as ever.

While the Allied command was debating which one of several alternatives to take as the pattern for the war in 1916, the Central Powers stole the initiative. General von Falkenhayn, Prussian chief-of-staff, given the choice of throwing the utmost resources of the German army into the capture of St. Petersburg—or Verdun—chose Verdun. The kaiser approved the decision, but German Chancellor Bethmann-Hollweg, inquired ironically: "Since when do you attack the enemy at his strongest point?"

Falkenhayn reasoned in a report to the emperor: "The strain on France has almost reached breaking point. If a major breakthrough could be made on the French front, England's best sword would be knocked out of her hand. . . . Within our reach behind the French sector of the Western front, there are objectives for the retention of which the French General Staff would be compelled to throw in every man they have. If they do so, the forces of France will bleed to death . . . as there can be no question of a voluntary withdrawal." Clearly Falkenhayn was not looking for a strategic advantage when he chose Verdun. He wanted a symbol which would be a challenge to French pride.

Verdun was a very ancient garrison town. It had been fortified as far back as the Romans. It was here in the medieval fortress that Charlemagne's grandsons in 843 divided his realm into three parts—so that, in a sense, Germany had been born at Verdun. Behind the modern struggle that was shaping up stretched a thousand years of Teuton-Gaul rivalry. There was historic justice, if nothing else, in the choice of Verdun for a showdown.

At the onset of the First World War, Verdun's outer forts had been allowed to deteriorate, and its defenses in general were in a bad state. Besides, after the reduction of Liege and Namur, fortresses had lost their prestige. Joffre believed that Verdun was an awkward salient and that the French position would be stronger without it. But there was no getting away from the popular concept in the French mind. Verdun was still the cornerstone of their defense, quite literally barring the road against the Germans.

The crown prince's artillery had been battering away at the outer line of forts which ringed Verdun proper since September of 1914, without making any appreciable dent. Then came orders from Falkenhayn. And while General Joffre was assuring the defenders of the fortress, "You will not be attacked. Verdun is not the point of the attack," the most powerful secret concentration of artillery ever seen in any war was being rushed to this German-occupied Meuse sector. Falkenhayn's directives to the crown prince had ordered him to economize on troops and slaughter the French with artillery fire. The imperial commander had proceeded to act upon these orders with unflagging zeal.

In the woods surrounding Verdun, gun pits had been dug at night. There was hardly room for a man to walk between massed cannon and ammunition dumps, all covered with camouflage nets and canvases. Thirteen "Big Berthas," the monster 420mm howitzer produced by Krupp which had pulverized the Belgian forts in short order, had been installed in the Forest of Spincourt. They were too enormous to transport in one piece, so they were dismantled before being trundled to the front. One "Big Bertha" filled twelve wagons and required 20 hours to prepare for action.

Besides, the Germans had brought up a number of brand new 280's that could fire a shell weighing 750 pounds over a distance of six miles. But one of the high-velocity guns they were depending upon most heavily in the Verdun assault was the 130mm howitzer. It was especially demoralizing to the enemy since the projectiles arrived simultaneously with the sound of the shot.

The crown prince had estimated there would be a grand artillery total of 1,220 pieces for an assault frontage of barely eight miles. The French might, in a pinch, put into action 300 heavy guns, including a few 270mm mortars, dating back to 1875. The assemblage of weapons was to be Germany's maximum effort of the war—artillery that would blast such a deep hole in the French lines the infantry would almost be able to reach the fort with rifles slung.

And all the while the French remained totally in the dark, without the slightest inkling of the batteries that were mushrooming in the wooded periphery of their frontline trenches. The Germans had recently broken up a spy network operated behind their lines by a Frenchwoman, Louise de Bettignies. When she and her sixty agents vanished, complete silence settled over the area so far as the French were concerned. And to further allay suspicion, the crown prince allowed only long-established guns, assumed to be already pinpointed on French artillery charts, to reply to enemy fire.

As His Imperial Highness continued his after-dinner stroll, he was pleased to note that nothing, not even the "Big Berthas" crouching under their camouflage nets, was visible in the billowy vacuum. Nor had transport ceased at nightfall. He felt a tingling of nerves at the crunch of wagon wheels bringing still more cannons, some from as far off as the Balkans, and the chug-chug of a little petrol-locomotive as it traveled a recently constructed spur track through the romantic woods, pulling a long train loaded with ammunition to provision the concealed guns.

Word that he would be in command of Germany's most crucial objective had reached the crown prince with dazzling suddenness. At court it was said the kaiser had never allowed him to develop a personality, and to date his army career had been far from brilliant. He had the reputation among his fellow officers of being woman-mad, and in a society as wholly masculine as the Prussians this was a decided drawback.

While touring occupied territory if a French girl waved to him as he was passing through a village, he would stop his bright red car in the middle of the street and invite her to take a ride. Encouraged by his sympathy, the girls would beseech him to help them locate some missing husband or sweetheart. Sometimes he obligingly made inquiries at German headquarters. Once he even sent a telegram to General Joffre. The German general staff was not only embarrassed but infuriated by such un-Prussian behavior. But with the preparations for the Verdun assault, the crown prince's outlook had taken on a new rigor. There was no more fraternizing with the enemy. There were no more French mistresses. Guns had become his sole preoccupation.

The whippets had dashed into the cauldron of mist to pursue some blazing scent, but returned at once to their master's muted whistle. All about him, in the raw, half-stifling air with its clandestine stir and rustle, the crown prince seemed to be listening to a mystic premonition of victory. His normally leaden gaze feverishly alight, he strode back to the farmhouse and, scarcely responding to the exaggerated salutes of his orderlies, retired at once to his quarters. Lighting his desk candle, he took a sheet of notepaper with the Hohenzollern crest and began a letter to his father, the kaiser.

"Sire, I will give you Verdun for a birthday present!"

For all their heady optimism there was something even German headquarters at Verdun did not know. The French were short on guns for the Champagne offensive, so they had stripped the Verdun forts of most of their batteries, with the exception of the immovable cannon in revolving turrets. Its defense system pruned to the minimum, Verdun continued into February of 1916, wholly unconscious of impending doom. Due to last-minute hitches in troop arrivals, the delivery of the kaiser's birthday gift was being postponed for a few weeks.

Then all was in readiness. And the assault, which went by the German secret code name of Operation Execution Place, was set for 12 February. After dark, on the night of the eleventh, elite German infantry shock troops stealthily took up their forward positions. The crown prince's main attacking force was comprised of three of the hardest hitting corps in the entire German army. While on the opposing side, the French XXXth Corps was said to be "composed of bric-a-brac." Thirty-four battalions of these French tag ends stood against seventy-two battalions that were notably the cream of the German forces.

On the morning of the twelfth, there was a blinding snowfall. Not even the *Nibelungs* could have devised anything so bad for a German attack. The artillerymen saw only white fleece through their range finders, and all day snow fell softly on the black snouts of the monster projectiles. The battle was scheduled for the following day, but heavy snow with rain and gales continued for over a week. One way or another the district lived up to its reputation of having the nastiest climate in the whole of France.

Finally, on the morning of 21 February, the Imperial German forces struck with a bombardment that took the French thoroughly by surprise. Every point in the Verdun sector received the same terrible pounding. In the Bois de Ville shells fell at a frequency of forty per minute. All the first positions were quickly carried by the Germans. And by afternoon an effective French command no longer existed.

In 1909, a French general staff representative on the Chamber of Deputies Budget Commission had declared: "You talk to us of heavy artillery. Thank God we have none!" The first day's fighting in the February assault at Verdun was to bear home the bitter irony of his boast. The French had plenty of the famous *soixante-quinzes,* the 75's which were France's pride. They were quicker firing, more accurate, and had a longer range than any other field gun of their day. Besides, they were mobile and only required three men to fire.

But in the Verdun attack, the 75's barely scraped the surface of German dugouts. And when the encircled French infantry sent up one supplicating rocket after another to their artillery to produce a 75 barrage, there was no response. The gunners could not see the rockets for the vaulting smoke of the German bombardment.

Reinforcements could not penetrate the barrage. The crude trench telephone system had been severed, and few runners made it through. French batteries were firing blindly. At 5 p.m. a German aviator returning to Fifth Army headquarters from a reconnaissance flight over the battle zone announced: "It's done. We can pass, there's nothing living there anymore."

The tremendous attacks upon Verdun continued throughout February. But at frightening cost the French held. Trying to make light of the bombardment, the *poilus* would say: *"Il pleut des marmites!"*—literally, "It rains cast-iron soup pots!" since this was almost the exact shape of the black shells. And then the thin assault lines of the French infantry, in their faded blue uniforms, would move to the attack.

Meanwhile an incident occurred at the fortress which would have curious, unforeseeable effects upon the fortunes of the entire siege. One of the usual swarm of neutral foreign correspondents had stopped at French headquarters. He chanced to mention the fact that spirits were high in Potsdam on account of a letter from the crown prince in which he promised the kaiser Verdun for a birthday present.

Words of the gibe spread until it reached the first-line trenches. And then by a kind of spontaneous combustion, the battlecry went up from one defensive position after another: *"Ils ne passeront pas! Ils ne passeront pas!"* "They shall not pass! They shall not pass!"

It was the miracle of Verdun, a revival of *élan vital,* the will to conquer, which had received such a mauling in the 1914 Battle of the Frontiers. Now its upsurge, for no apparent reason, the will to hold shook the complacency of the German command. But then the Germans never had understood *élan vital.* They put their faith in timetables, reservists, right flank encirclements, and heavy guns. By all obvious reckoning French morale should have been at zero. They could not know it owed its fatal resuscitation, its almost demoniac determination, to an imprudent note written in a moment of brimming enthusiasm by their own commander-in-chief.

General Chretien, in command of Verdun, had called the battle zone *"un terrain catastrophe."* All the same the French had begun to find advantages in this chaos of shattered woods. Working forward in small groups supported by machine-gun fire, the infantry used the land with pronounced tactical skill.

But summer brought such intense heat that thirst proved an even worse torment than the exploding shells. Water carriers starting out with twenty pails for a company in an advanced post, after traveling over torn-up shelled ground, would be lucky to arrive with ten—and then the water smelled of corpses. Everything had this odor of putrefaction owing to the fact that the earth was literally stuffed with bodies. Later it was calculated that 150,000 dead, both French and German, were never buried but simply absorbed into the ground.

Out of the fierce fighting in June came one of the enduring legends of the First World War—that of the *Tranchée des Baionnettes.* Number 3 Company of the 137th French Infantry Regiment was guarding a Ravine de la Dame on the approach to one of the outer forts. Shells rained heavily upon the area all night, and in the morning there was no trace of Number 3 Company.

Only after the war was the trench finally discovered which the company had occupied. It was completely filled in, but from one part of it rifles protruded at regular intervals, bayonets still fixed to rusty muzzles. After excavation, a corpse was found beneath each rifle. The company had apparently placed its rifles on the parapet, ready to repel an attack, and rather than abandon their position had been buried alive to a man by the German bombardment—again a grim echo of "They shall not pass!"

Nine villages around Verdun vanished in the opening bombardments. And when the rains came, sections of the denuded woods had been churned up so many times by bursting shells, the mud was like a quicksand in which troops, weighted down with heavy packs, sank and drowned.

By summer commanders on both sides had sickened of the senseless struggle and would gladly have washed their hands of it. Joffre grumbled over the hopeless waste of men and materials, out of all proportion to the strategic value of the citadel, and then borrowed still more precious guns from Verdun for his approaching Sommes offensive.

Even the iron mouths of the gigantic 420's were wearing out from too much continual firing, but the men went on. Then at the end of June the Germans played their trump card. This time General von Knobelsdorf was so positive his attack as planned would achieve a breakthrough to the city of Verdun itself, he ordered up the colors and bands of the various regiments for a triumphal entry. A special invitation was sent to the kaiser to be present to watch the fall of Verdun from Fifth Army Headquarters.

The invitations being promptly accepted, the Supreme War Lord and his entourage arrived at the farmhouse at Stenay-sur-Meuse, where French champagne was on ice for the expected celebration. It was noted that greetings between father and son were unusually cordial. After all the kaiser was about to receive his birthday present, or at least the belated remnants of it.

Although the emperor's moods were as volatile as ever, ranging from elation to manic depression, the prolongation of the war had unquestionably chastened him. The fair curly hair was iron grey, and as a friend remarked, "His face has completely changed, having stiffened as though the life had gone out of it." He would be found in tears in corners of churches all over the Rhineland, praying for hours.

Still he continued to impersonate the Supreme War Lord. And while his absolutism had become a myth, and his generals only paid lip service to his authority, he traveled endlessly in the cream and gold imperial train between Eastern and Western fronts. He was a nuisance in combat zones, but he kept turning up, visiting the trenches and bestowing medals. He passed out so many, the saying went, the only way to avoid receiving an iron cross, second class, was to commit suicide.

The French were enjoying the spell of unusually fine weather when, on the evening of 23 June, all the German guns suddenly ceased firing. In the uncanny silence, the defensive lines of infantry developed a bad case of nerves. For once their own guns went unanswered. And then they heard a multitude of soft whistlings overhead, like birds cleaving the air and then dropping by swarms into ravines to the rear. In every sector, the German shells, all marked with a green cross, fell silently. But soon after the mystery was explained as a sickening odor of putrefaction pervaded the battle zone, followed by the strangling sensations of gas.

The German scientists had perfected a new formula known as phosgene or "Green Cross Gas" as the German army called it because of the shell markings. One of the deadliest gases ever used in warfare, it made its debut at Verdun. Although the French whipped on their masks, the asphyxiating fumes of the new gas still managed to leak through.

Packhorses frothed at the mouth and went into convulsions; none of the supplies of cartridges and water which the frontline infantry had been calling for frantically all night could get through the gas curtain. As the fumes drifted to the rear areas, the French batteries were paralyzed. And the gunners who survived resembled green corpses.

The gas shelling ceased as abruptly as it began, and the high explosives took over once more. Then, at daybreak, according to schedule, the German infantry advanced in densest formations the French had ever seen, their reserves following close behind. It was to have been the knockout blow. But fortunately for the defense, the gas had settled in hollows and so failed to incapacitate the French batteries on higher ground. These now went into deadly action.

Even a carrier pigeon was infected with *La Gloire*. A colonel trapped with the remnants of his regiment in a gas-filled subterranean passage beneath one of the forts tried to dispatch his last pigeon to the fortress with a plea for relief. The badly gassed bird fluttered about helplessly, but was finally coaxed into the air. It reached headquarters, was delivered of its message, and fell dead. Afterward it was decorated with the ribbon of the Legion of Honor, stuffed, and placed in a Paris museum.

The Germans had found one couldn't kill everyone. As their infantry came forward, there was always a machine gun in the end of a trench, a grenade thrower in a shell hole, a section which rallied in the hell of a ravaged wood.

The fatal days of 23-24 June passed, and still there was no breakthrough to Verdun. The preparations for the triumphal entry were hushed up, and in disgust the kaiser returned to Potsdam. In military terms, the resistance of the all but pulverized French defenses was inexplicable. On three occasions the Germans might have taken Verdun by outright capture: on 25-26 February, 8-12 June, and 23-24 June. Even Foch said of his enemy that they were "the most splendid army in the world."

Their preparations for the assault had been masterful. Had they succeeded, the fall of Verdun would have led to the "rolling-up" of the whole Western Front. But some transcendent, mystic power held them at bay. After the war, a sculptured lion was placed at La Chapelle Sainte-Fine, marking "the farthest point reached by the Germans before Verdun." They came very near, but they did not pass.

Modern classes from the Paris *Ecole des Militaires* are taken on tours of the fortress of Verdun and its perimeter that lessons may be learned from this worst of all battles—the one with highest density of dead per square yard ever fought. But for the most part, the lessons of Verdun are of an elusive sort, not easily transmitted from one generation to the next.

Stalingrad

by Angela Stuart

In December of 1941 Hitler dismissed Walter von Brauchitsch, commander-in-chief of the German army or Wehrmacht, because of the general's hostility to the Nazi invasion of Russia. With the post of supreme commander of the army empty, Hitler promptly assumed it himself. To the press he remarked, "This little affair of operational command is something anyone can do." He went on to say he would direct operations according to his intuition.

The men who wore the coveted wine-red stripes of the general staff officer were shocked to the core at the idea of an Austrian corporal issuing directives to Prussian generals. But in the end they swallowed their pride. There was a good deal to be said for Hitler's "intuition," or at least his intuitive sense of timing. So far it had stacked up an impressive array of conquests: Poland, Czechoslovakia, Norway, Denmark, the Low Countries, Greece, and France.

And even if the Nazi invasion of Russia in the summer and fall of 1941 had not resulted in the expected "knife-through-butter" victory, from all indications Soviet resistance was crumbling. Two to three million Russian soldiers had surrendered to the Germans in the first drive on Moscow. Hundreds of thousands were killed. Most of Russia's iron and coal areas were occupied. The Germans held a line from near Leningrad on the Baltic Sea in the north to near Odessa on the Black Sea in the south.

Long before, Napoleon had written from a Russian bivouac: "This is a bad business. I beat the Russians every time, but that doesn't get me anywhere." If there was a warning in the spectre of the French campaign of 1812, the Fuehrer failed to heed it. After all, Napoleon's legions had braved the Russian colossus on foot. In Hitler's new army everything was mobile. Even the artillery, by means of tractors or motorized mountings, was as mobile as the armor and the infantry.

The Fuehrer was so possessed by the old German dream of "*Drang nach Osten*"—"Push to the East!"—that in June of 1942 he threw 70 percent of his armed might, 240 infantry and armored divisions, into the battle to conquer Russia. The first goal of the great summer offensive of 1942, known as "Operation Blue," was the Caucasus and its oil fields, since gasoline shortages had already developed in the Third Reich. The city of Stalingrad was only a marginal consideration.

Then Hitler changed his mind and his plans. Stalingrad dominated the Volga, which was Russia's principal artery. Millions of tons of food, oil, machinery, and American lend-lease equipment passed up this vital waterway to Moscow. If Hitler captured Stalingrad he could control the Volga and starve the Russian capital. So the city shifted from a subsidiary role—a stepping-stone to the Caucasus—to become in itself a prime objective.

The capture of Stalingrad had been entrusted to General Friedrich von Paulus' Sixth Army which had blitzed its way through Belgium, Holland, and France. Von Paulus himself, at 52, was a striking figure—six feet, six inches in height, pale, thin-lipped, with a nervous twitch in his right eye. While born in Hesse and not East Prussia, he was still the Prussian staff officer *par excellence,* "unconditionally reliable and cold to the heart."

At the very outset of the offensive Sixth Army met with a grave mishap. On June 19 an operations officer with the Twenty-second Panzer Division was shot down in a reconnaissance plane over an area between the Russian and German lines. He carried a secret German order outlining the attack plan. The Germans immediately sent out scout troops to search the terrain. They found the wreckage of the plane, but no trace of the operations officer or of the plans. It was clear the Russians had both and so knew exactly where and when they might expect an attack. Nevertheless, the plans were not changed, and Sixth Army proceeded according to schedule.

As the German panzers rumbled eastward, slicing, probing, and thrusting deep into Soviet territory, they discovered, like Napoleon, that vast mileages covered meant little on the great Russian plains. While Red losses were enormous, German losses were also high. And there was no hope of a Sedan, the single decisive battle of the nineteenth century—only more miles of dusty plains and more Russians.

But although the Germans lost fifty to a hundred tanks every day, they never stopped. "Experienced dead were replaced by inexperienced living," and tenuously held supply lines kept on lengthening. Then in July occurred what postwar German military writers have called "the single most tragic error in the battle for Stalingrad."

The Russians had been withdrawing steadily before the German advance. Middle and lower commanders had lost control of their chopped-up units. In many sectors there was wild flight. Then suddenly Russian rear guards reported: "No more enemy contact." The Germans were not following close on their heels. There was no sign of von Paulus' spearheads. Deeply puzzled, the Soviets immediately contacted their espionage, who were kept well informed by a leak in the German high command. But intelligence knew nothing of any change in Hitler's plans.

The reason for the halt was simple. Sixth Army had run out of gas. It took two gallons of fuel to move one tank one mile. In a sudden switch Hitler had sent the major part of the fuel supplies earmarked for Sixth Army to the Caucasus. So the bulk of the army remained immobilized on the Kalmyk steppes for eighteen days.

No delay could have been more vital to the Russians. Working feverishly, they used the eighteen days to bring up reserves and to build defensive positions along the northern approaches to Stalingrad. Stalin had allowed his generals to withdraw from the Donets and the Don, but he now drew a line at the Volga. On July 12 he issued his famous directive: "I order the formation of an Army Group Stalingrad. The city itself will be defended by Sixty-second Army to the last man."

In August Sixth Army tanks forced their way across the Don, the best defense line in southern Russia, by means of a complete cooperation between Nazi ground command and the Luftwaffe. While German bombers machine-gunned and bombed every road within a radius of thirty to forty miles to hold back Red Army reserves from attacking, Nazi engineers frantically laid pontoon bridges. They skillfully sank the bridges under two feet of water to conceal them from Russian planes. But the shallow water did not bar the passage of German tanks and trucks.

On August 23, in the evening, Panzer Grenadiers of the Sixteenth Panzer Division, Sixth Army, reached the Volga in strength. The forward tanks caught their first glimpse of the skyline of Stalingrad. Commanders standing up in their turrets saw the elongated ribbon city strung out for some thirty miles along the high bluffs on the west bank of the Volga. Factory smokestacks loomed up, tall blocks of buildings, and onion-spired cathedrals, with clouds of smoke here and there where Stukas were bombing barracks and road intersections.

At the time of the invasion the population of Stalingrad, including peripheral villages, was around seven hundred thousand. The terrain was made even more irregular by the river Tsaritza which ran through the middle of the city. Its deep gorge cut Stalingrad into a northern and southern half, with factories in the north and shops, office buildings, and apartments in the south.

The tanks roared forward, their tracks crunching through the dry grass of the steppe. Without warning an artillery salvo of heavy flak came from the northern outskirts of the city. The battalion fired back, scoring one direct hit after another against the gun emplacements, until all thirty-seven guns with their crews were shattered.

Curiously enough, the panzers had suffered hardly any losses. As soon as the Germans penetrated the smashed gun emplacements the reason became apparent. To their horror, they discovered that the heavy antiaircraft guns had been manned wholly by women from the "Red Barricade" ordnance factory. They had received rudimentary training in antiaircraft defense, but since they had no idea how to use their guns against ground targets they had been wiped out.

Hitler had concentrated an entire air fleet under the command of General Wolfram Baron von Richthofen, son of the World War I ace, against the lone city on the Volga. As German infantry prongs pushed into Stalingrad from a dozen angles, everything was burning and collapsing. Even the Volga was covered with a sheet of flame from exploded oil tanks.

Peripheral villages had been wiped out. Pitomnik was famous for its fruit tree nursery where the highest grade pear and cherry trees were grown. But village and nursery were a shambles. Nothing remained but the Pitomnik airstrip, jammed with ack-ack guns.

As the Germans penetrated the deeply echeloned, fortified approaches to the city, Soviet resistance became suicidal. Red soldiers obeying the slogan "Every man a fortress!" tied grenades around their waists and threw themselves under the oncoming tanks. Factory workers laid down their tools, took guns from the assembly line, and opened fire on the enemy. Tanks without paint or gunsights were driven straight out of tractor works into battle.

But nothing could stem the Nazi advance, the smooth battle cooperation between the three main arms —tanks, infantry, and artillery. On September 27, the German breakthrough to central Stalingrad was accomplished under the impact of 1000-a-day bomber raids.

Wild with joy, drunken Nazis jumped off trucks, playing mouth organs, bellowing and dancing on the pavement between the shells of five and six story office buildings. Russians watched from houses, cellars, firing points. At the same time, on the perimeter of the city, Stuka formations, returning from raids, dipped low over their own armored ground attack, exuberantly sounding their sirens.

Victory was in the air, but not for long. Stalin had

sent his last personal reserves to the defense of the city that bore his name—the elite Thirteenth Guard Division under the command of General Rodimentsev. Battling the Germans to recapture central Stalingrad, Rodimentsev's 10,000 guardsmen stood firm to the last extremity. There was no retreat. Only the heavily wounded crawled away.

The Germans had invented a phrase, "the battle that has no morrow," to describe the ideal engagement. But Stalingrad had nothing but "morrows," each one grimmer than the last. Throughout the autumn the Germans inched ahead through a labyrinth of rubble. Fighting for Stalingrad North was the fiercest and most costly of the war. The Germans had cut off the city from three sides only. The Russians could still enter from the river behind. They knew their own city, even though it was a shambles, and so had the advantage in the street fighting.

Every shell hole, shattered house, or crack in a wall was a hard point of resistance. Men fought desperately to take a broom closet. Battles raged in corridors of office buildings. Not since World War I was an expenditure in ammunition so enormous. To the outside world, it was not clear at any time where the Russians were and where the Germans were.

The Russians cleverly reduced no-man's-land to a minimum. It never exceeded the distance of a hand-grenade throw. Through this close combat tactic they nullified the effectiveness of German aircraft. The crews, never good at precision bombing, were afraid of hitting their own troops. Nor could tanks operate through mountains of rubble.

Odd relics survived the general demolition. The enormously high factory chimneys still raked the sky—chimneys being hard to hit—although the factories themselves were in ruins. And in a downtown square stone statues of children danced around a fountain, although heads and arms had been shot off.

Hitler was becoming impatient. From his personal command post near the village of Cinnitsa in the Ukraine, he radioed von Paulus: "This job's got to be finished. The city must finally be taken."

The chief reason Stalingrad was not finally taken was that the Red Army's last reserves, fresh, rested troops, were thrown into the ruins that had been turned into a fortress. Von Paulus, on the other hand, received no reserves with the exception of five engineer battalions flown out from Germany for the street fighting. All the replacements for his bled-white regiments had to come from within his army's zone of operations. The appalling truth was that Hitler had overextended himself to the point where he did not have a single reserve division on the entire Eastern Front.

The Red Army headquarters was a dugout in the Tsaritza gorge. Here, their backs to the rock cliffs of the Volga, Lieutenant-General Vasili Chuikov and his tough Sixty-second Siberians were entrusted with the defense of Stalingrad. It was no longer a revolutionary army. The salute and epaulettes, banished in 1917, were back. The new uniform closely resembled that worn by czarist troops. Nor did a private any longer address a general as "Tovarich."

Chuikov was one of the younger Russian generals. Heavyset, with thick black hair, he grinned often, exposing a double row of gold teeth. But despite his sense of humor, his rages were feared almost as much as Hitler's. He had been in Stalingrad before at the very outset of his military career when he had fought the White Russian forces under General Denikin. It had been touch and go then, and now the situation was even more grave.

The staff map of the battle had become a map of the city. Distances were no longer measured in kilometers, but meters. The front was a matter of street corners, blocks, and individual buildings. The German attacks were entered in blue; the Russian defensive positions, in red. The blue arrows were getting ever closer to Red battle headquarters.

With the swastika flying over the center of Stalingrad, Chuikov said: "Time is blood." The phrase would epitomize the Russian defense. They fought not for victory, but for time—time to bring up their last reserves, time to wear out the Germans.

Winter comes early to the steppes, with twilight at two o'clock. The Russians were at least prepared, with felt boots, padded jackets, fur hats, skis, and sleighs. But due to a ghastly mistake on the part of the German high command, several trains of winter clothing and equipment for Sixth Army were stalled somewhere far from Stalingrad.

On the perimeter of the city, weak German battalions had their frozen and exhausted troops out on the steppes that afforded no cover. Russian infantrymen kept infiltrating German positions. In their white camouflage capes, they were invisible against the snow. The Germans were black targets for every bullet.

On November 8, 1942, after his casualty reports were in, General von Wietershem, commander of the XIVth Panzer Corps, informed von Paulus: "If the present situation continues, I can tell you the exact day on which I will lose my last man."

Von Paulus sent an urgent message to Hitler, requesting permission to "break off the attack and withdraw Sixth Army to a fortified winter line extending from Kharkov to Rostov." There was still time.

The Fuehrer's refusal was adamant. He based his defense upon an obsolete linear concept. Ignoring the shattered condition of German divisions and the immense difficulties of supply, he was always unwilling to yield ground or shorten a front. Besides, he continued to underrate the "sub-humans" of Russia while overestimating the Western Allies.

He kept four magnificently equipped, major, mobile formations tied down in Southern France in fear of an invasion that was twenty months away. Had they been transferred to the Stalingrad front, Chuikov and his troops on the Volga bank would not have stood up for forty-eight hours.

The atmosphere at German supreme headquarters in the Ukraine steadily worsened. General Zeitzler, chief of the general staff, called it "not only weird but positively incredible." Arguments, recriminations, and a raging spate of words were the daily fare. Stalingrad had become a monomania with Hitler.

Because of his insistence upon overcentralized command, he was issuing detailed orders to battle commanders from hundreds of miles away. His intervention in tactical matters violated their professional standards. And on the highest strategical level, general staff officers were operating in a void to the point of unreason. If informed of a defeat, the Fuehrer called it "idiotic twaddle," and, his mouth foaming, threatened the unfortunate bearer of the news with physical violence. The "mad genius" had now veered, it seemed, almost entirely to madness.

On November 19, the Russians launched their attack against the Rumanian Third Army which was protecting von Paulus' flank along the Don. It was Russian weather from the start. Rain, snow, and freezing fog made all Luftwaffe operations near the river impossible.

For eighty minutes annihilating fire was concentrated on one two-mile area of the Rumanian line. Then at eight a.m. Russian tanks rolled out of hidden positions in the Kremenskaya forest. They came on fifty abreast, wave on wave. The tanks, T-34's and American-made Shermans, were covered with infantrymen like ants on a lump of sugar, their pockets bulging with grenades and ribbons of ammunition over their shoulders. In their hands they clutched the cheap but devasting little Russian machine-guns. The Rumanian Army was torn to shreds.

On the afternoon of November 23, the Red Third Guards Mechanized Corps, driving down from the north, met the Fifth Guards Mechanized Corps from the south. They joined forces near Kalach on the Don bend. As green flares went up, the converging units understood what had happened. Wild with excitement, they hugged and kissed one another.

Von Paulus' Sixth Army had been completely encircled. It was catastrophe for a quarter million troops on the Volga. Von Paulus' forces, including most of the German elements of the Fourth Panzer Army, parts of the Rumanian divisions, Luftwaffe units, and some 70,000 noncombatants, were trapped in the Stalingrad pocket.

The Russians were not brilliant strategists, but they did exploit German blunders. Stalin, aware that von Paulus' flanks were protected by flimsy, ill-equipped Rumanian and Italian allies, ordered frontal attacks on both wings, which were easily penetrated.

At German headquarters, General Zeitzler used all the pressure he dared to try to pursuade his Fuehrer to order an immediate breakout attempt by Sixth Army. German commanders inside and outside Stalingrad knew that the Russian forces surrounding them were thin. But if Sixth Army was to burst free, it had to pick up, leave Stalingrad, and attack west with all possible strength before the Russian band was reinforced.

Hitler, in a fury, crashed his fist down on a table, shouting, "I won't leave the Volga. I won't go back from the Volga." To von Paulus he sent orders to move his headquarters from the outskirts of the city into the heart of Stalingrad, to form a hedgehog (all-around defense), and hold fast.

In its new role, the shattered city was dubbed "Fortress Stalingrad." But it was an ill-equipped fortress. Men were burrowed into broken walls, piles of brick, parts of houses, ruined factories. They died at the rate of one thousand a day in December, fifteen-hundred a day in January—of wounds, exposure, starvation, disease.

Hermann Goering, chief of the Luftwaffe, had promised to supply the minimum five-hundred tons a day of food, clothing, and ammunition which von Paulus said he would require to keep Sixth Army in some sort of fighting condition. But it turned out to be a rash promise.

Stalingrad lay in a weather "pocket" at the edge of a meteorological frontier which severely hampered flying. Icing up and poor visibility caused more casualties than enemy action. One plane in every three was lost. No air power on earth could have sustained such a drain. Pilots, refusing to land, had their crews kick the supplies out of cargo doors. Much of it was lost.

Late in November, Field Marshal Fritz Erich von Manstein, rated the ablest German commander of World War II, was given the task of breaking through the Russian encirclement and rescuing the 200,000 men still alive in "Fortress Stalingrad." Von Manstein hurriedly took command of a newly created "Army Group Don" composed of ragtag units outside the Stalingrad ring. The ring of steel had now thickened to some thirty to sixty kilometers.

To stiffen Army Group Don and to provide a spearhead of fresh troops, Sixth Panzer Division was ordered from far-off Brittany. The eighty trains that moved the division were delayed by blown bridges, ripped-up rails, and guerrilla attacks. So they arrived late.

By December 15, von Manstein's panzers had driven through blinding snow to within thirty miles of "Fortress Stalingrad." The troops could see the signal flares of desperate men at the southern end of the trap.

But December 21 the German attack stalled. Further advance was impossible. The Red Army was rushing in from all sides. The rescue force itself was in danger of being cut off. Without asking Hitler's permission, von Manstein radioed von Paulus, ordering him to break out toward the rescue units within twenty-four hours. At this time, generals inside the pocket had already taken steps to prepare for a breakthrough.

All that stood between Sixth Army and salvation was thirty miles as the crow flies (forty or forty-five miles by road). But von Paulus was a pure strategist, not a rebel. He knew that von Manstein was acting upon his own authority. Without a direct order from Hitler he would not move. He gave as his excuse that he had only enough fuel to take his vehicles twenty miles.

Early in December the quartermaster-general at a German supply depot near the Polish border had gathered together huge stocks of wine, brandy, gourmet cheeses, chocolate, jams, and thousands of pounds of rich cake baked in Poland on German orders. It was to be a Christmas treat for Sixth Army.

But the delicacies never arrived. Instead, inside Stalingrad, the order was issued on Christmas Eve to slaughter 6000 of the emaciated horses still in the city. They were killed, butchered, and the hunks stewed for hours in huge pots. The meat was eaten with a special ration of a half pound of bread. The hot broth was saved and served the next day with four slices of bread as a full ration.

It was a grim Christmas. Along the perimeter, troops drank "German tea" or melted snow. On Hill 135, the highest point in Stalingrad, a little pine decorated with paper ornaments and a few candles glimmered for an hour before mortar fire destroyed it. In the icy cellars and dugouts, a few soldiers sang *"Sheilige nacht."* Others listened to carols from distant Germany until the music was interrupted by static and the voice of Radio Moscow: "Every seven seconds a German soldier dies in Russia. Stalingrad . . . mass grave. One-two-three-four-five-six-seven . . . every seven seconds a German soldier dies."

On January 8, two Russian officers, accompanied by a bugler and carrying a white flag, approached the German lines. The bugle sounded and the Germans answered with a hail of fire. The Red officers scampered to cover, then returned, waving their flag and sounding their bugle. This time the Germans were silent.

The Russians were blindfolded and led into the enemy camp. They delivered a message to von Paulus from the Russian high command:

"All hopes that your troops might be saved by the German offensive from the south have collapsed. The German troops rushed to your assistance have been routed and are now retreating toward Rostov.

"The hard Russian winter is only beginning. The deep frosts, cold winds and blizzards are still to reach their full force, and your soldiers are not protected with warm clothes and live in unhygienic conditions.

"As Commander you must fully realize that you have no possibility of breaking through the ring that surrounds you. Your position is hopeless and further resistance is useless. In view of the hopeless position you face, and in order to avoid unnecessary bloodshed, we offer you the following terms of surrender":

(Conventional terms followed.)

"In the event of the rejection of this proposal by you, we now warn that the Red Army troops and Red Airforce will be compelled to take steps to wipe out the surrounded German troops, and that you will be responsible for their annihilation." The signature was that of Lieutenant-General Konstantin Rokossovsky, commander of the Don Front.

Within minutes Hitler's answer snapped back to the

single remaining radio receiving unit in Stalingrad: "Surrender is forbidden. Sixth Army will hold its positions until the last man and the last round of ammunition and by their heroic endurance will make an unforgettable contribution towards the establishment of a defensive front and the salvation of the western world."

For weeks the Austrian Forty-fourth Infantry Division under Major Pohl had been holding the approaches to Stalingrad's most vital airfield, Pitomnik. As a reward for his heroic resistance, the major had received the Knight's Cross. With the order, von Paulus had sent a little package with "best wishes" written on it in his own hand. Inside was a loaf of army bread and a tin of herrings in tomato sauce. On the Eastern Front the herrings counted for far more than the highest decoration for gallantry. But on January 14, the Austrian Infantry was crushed in its own positions. Pitomnik fell. On January 23, the Stalingradski airstrip was overrun by the Reds, and Sixth Army lost its last physical link with the outside world. The pocket was now compressed to an area fifteen miles long by nine miles deep. Sixth Army was battered on all sides by elements of seven Soviet armies.

But the Germans fought on. In January the temperature dropped to 35 degrees below zero, centigrade. But centigrade or Fahrenheit, the cold was paralyzing. The blood of the wounded froze to red ice.

Hospitals were in unheated basements. The Germans had run out of drugs, dressings, plasma, anesthetic. A doctor ordered that one-hundred-forty-one men whom he judged to be hopelessly wounded be carried from a cellar and placed outside in the snow. At least in this way they might die in the warm glow that comes with freezing to death.

The scale of fighting had shrunk from divisions to battalions, and from battalions to squads. Four of these squads, of from five to eight Germans each, were defending a snowy field on a January night when they heard the rumble of Russian tanks. They had only rifles, and several of the men, scrambling out of their shallow trench, made a run for it. But they were silhouetted black against the white field and bullets quickly cut them down.

In another mudhole, four riflemen crazed with fear but not daring to run, tried to flatten themselves into the ground. They heard the approaching tank cut its speed. It crept forward until it straddled the saucer-shaped hole. The men screamed in terror, but the Russian at the throttle threw his tank into gear and gave it full power.

The cleated tracks dug through the snow into the mud before the driver cut the power. Instantly he threw the machine into reverse and the tracks ground deeper into the mud. Then he spun the tank to left and right. As it sank deeper, its tracks ground through flesh, blood, and bone, and the screaming stopped.

On January 23, Major von Zitzewitz, who had been posted at Stalingrad as an observer for the high command, was flown out of the pocket that he might deliver his last report to Hitler in person. He was ushered into a spacious, dimly lit room at German headquarters in the Ukraine. There was a large, circular gable surrounded by club chairs, a huge situation map of the entire Eastern Front tacked to one wall, and a blazing log fire in the grate.

Von Zitzewitz, as an emissary from hell itself, must have been struck by the contrast with the type of headquarters he had just left. In Stalingrad there were no tables, chairs, fireplaces. Company commanders and staff officers lay in the filth of freezing basements and dugouts, wounded, feverish, with ulcerations and dysentery, not knowing what to do.

Hitler came forward to meet the major, taking his right hand and gripping it in both of his. "You've come from a deplorable situation," he said.

Then, leading the way to the map, he began speaking with animation of his future plans for Sixth Army. If they could just hold out until spring—he was forming a battalion to be made up entirely of new Panther tanks. (His former pride and joy had been the Tiger tank, but they had proved too ungainly for mobile tactics. They had the tonnage but not the horsepower for a running fight.) The Panther battalion would attack straight through the enemy towards Stalingrad, in order to ferry supplies through in this way and to reinforce Sixth Army by tanks.

Von Zitzewitz was thunderstruck by such daydreaming. A single tank battalion was to launch a successful attack across hundreds of miles of strongly held enemy territory, when an entire panzer army had been unable to accomplish the feat!

With all the ardor at his command, the major pleaded for the dying army. "My Fuehrer," he ended, "permit me to state that the troops at Stalingrad can no longer be ordered to fight to their last round because they are no longer physically capable of fighting, and because they no longer have a last round."

Hitler seemed to look straight through him. Then he said: "Man recovers very quickly."

The interview was over. To Stalingrad, the Fuehrer radioed: "Surrender out of the question. Troops will resist to the end." Then, as an afterthought, he promoted von Paulus to the rank of field marshal. No German field marshal in history had ever been taken alive.

On January 31, 1943, Sixth Army Headquarters in the basement of the Univermag department store on Stalingrad's Red Square sent its last message: "The Russians stand at the door of our bunker. We are destroying our equipment."

The Germans then raised a small white flag on the

street level. The square was already surrounded by Red battalions. Russian soldiers approached cautiously. They were told to fetch a ranking officer to whom von Paulus could honorably surrender. Russian general staff officers, newsmen, and photographers rushed to the scene.

Von Paulus, haggard, but impeccably dressed, emerged to give himself up. With him into captivity went twenty-three generals, two thousand to twenty-five hundred officers, and almost ninety-thousand enlisted men—all that was left of Sixth Army.

Leaflets giving the news of the capitulation were quickly printed by the Soviets and dropped on twenty-five thousand Germans still holding out at the northern end of Stalingrad. On February 2, they, too, gave up. The surrender was complete and unconditional.

According to Sixth Army operation diaries now in American custody, there were two-hundred-thirty-thousand German and German allied troops in the pocket as of December 18, 1942. Of these, some forty-two-thousand wounded, sick, and specialists were evacuated by air up to January 24, 1943. Of the approximate one-hundred-twenty-thousand who surrendered, it has been estimated fifty-thousand died in the first two months of imprisonment in Russian camps. To date fewer than six-thousand veterans of the surrender have ever returned to Germany.

Stalingrad is rated the greatest defeat in military history. Certainly it was the crucial battle of World War II, the turning point for the Western Allies. Hitler's best divisions had been destroyed, and although his armies would go on fighting German arrogance had received a setback from which it would never recover.

The home front had been kept in stark ignorance of the true condition of von Paulus' trapped Sixth Army. When news of the surrender broke upon the Third

Reich, the shock was overwhelming. Throughout Germany for three days, radio stations played the Siegfried Funeral March from the *Gotterdammerung* . . . over and over again.

The Battle of Berlin

by Lillian Morris and Philip Procter

September 1, 1939, dawned cloudy and gray over Berlin. As the city slept, German armies crossed the Polish border and, for the second time in a quarter of a century, war descended upon Europe. By 10:30, the skies over the German capital were clearing, as Adolf Hitler—immaculate in black trousers and field gray tunic—passed down the sun-dappled *Unter den Linden* on the way from his massive, pink Reich Chancellery to the Kroll Opera House where the members of the Reichstag had been hastily assembled. Except for the spotless SS guards standing at attention at intervals along the curb, there were few Berliners on the street to witness the Fuehrer's ride.

The ornate Kroll Opera House, with its red carpeting, wine-colored walls, and a spotlighted silver eagle behind the speaker's rostrum, was a fitting backdrop for

Hitler's declaration of war: "This night Polish soldiers fired on German territory. Since 5:45 o'clock this morning, the fire has been returned!"

Berliners, hearing the speech from loudspeakers set up on almost every street corner throughout the city, despaired. This Declaration of War, unlike that of 1914, brought from them no cheers—too many could remember that earlier war!

Berlin at the end of World War I had been a city torn by strikes, demonstrations, and anarchy, as it teetered toward economic collapse. Following the armistice, the city had borne the burden of reparations, assimilated the influx of war veterans and refugees, protected the new German Republic against right and left wing coups, cleaned the municipal government of corruption following Mayor Gustav Boss' retirement in 1929, weathered the depression, and, on 30 January, 1933, watched helplessly as a forty-three-year-old Austrian by the name of Adolf Hitler became chancellor of Germany.

The typically cynical Berliners who witnessed the mammoth Nazi torchlight victory parade that night knew that a majority of the singing Brown Shirts had been imported from outside of Berlin. Not enough SA troops could be mustered in the city to put on an impressive show. Besides, the Berliners said, as they listened to the menacing tramp of the marching boots, "Those farmers have bigger feet."

That a majority of Berliners were anti-Nazi was evidenced by the facts that the National Socialists never once carried Berlin in a free election and that, even after the NSDAP had come to power in March, 1933, only 86 Nazi assemblymen were able to win seats in the 222-member city council.

"Red Berlin," the Nazi called the liberal city. But they could hardly ignore it, for its area equalled that of the Ruhr Basin, it had a population of nearly four

Adolf Hitler.

Hitler watching maneuvers. (UPI)

Hitzkirchen

and one-half million, and it was the political, commercial, and financial center of Germany. "Whoever controls Berlin controls the Reich!" Joseph Goebbels, the "dark dwarf" of National Socialism had said. Because of this obvious truth, the Nazis—like rejected but determined suitors—continued to woo the Berliners. Indeed, even while they were bludgeoning their victims into submission, they went on whispering "sweet nothings" into their ears!

The National Socialists had appointed Joseph Goebbels Gauleiter of Berlin in 1929. In 1933, the Nazis took control of the city government by appointing a special state commissioner to whom the lord mayor was accountable. In 1935, the mayor was simply replaced with a city president appointed by Adolf Hitler.

Catalog files containing information cards on every "suspect" Berliner covered one entire wall from ceiling to floor of the Gestapo headquarters on Prinz Albrecht Strasse. SS barracks were spread throughout the city, and a concentration camp, Sachsenhausen, was constructed only twenty miles north of Berlin.

In six years (1933-1939), the Nazis succeeded in warping the appearance of Berlin from that of a cosmopolitan metropolis into that of a stridently Germanic capital and, by overt and constant harassment and terrorism, had frightened its citizens into at least a semblance of subjugation. Berlin became a city of "whispers." The quick glance over the shoulder to make sure that no other person was within hearing distance of a shared joke about, or a disparaging remark against, the regime became known as the "German look," and stuffing up the mouthpiece of the telephone before embarking upon an honest conversation within the confines of one's own home was an automatic action.

With the declaration of war against Poland, however, the Berliners' long-smoldering rage at the Nazis flared into the open again, and, when Britain and

France joined the war against Germany on 3 September, an open revolt by Berlin's implacable women seemed imminent.

From all over the city came their loudly voiced criticisms of the regime, their open defiance of the Nazis. They began by complaining about the food rationing which had gone into effect on 28 August. That was followed by resentment over the air raid alerts which sent them stumbling through the blackout into basements and subway shelters, where they had to spend sleep-robbing hours while anti-aircraft searchlights practiced sweeping an empty sky. From this it was but a step to taking action against a war they did not want, a war which would take the lives of their husbands and sons.

In the western suburb of Kopenick women threw themselves in front of troop trains to keep them from leaving Berlin for the front. Count Wolf von Helldorf's Berlin police had to club the protesters and physically drag them from the tracks. From then on, it was necessary to entrain troops clandestinely and move them from the city under cover of darkness.

The angry talk continued unabated. Adolf Hitler was crazy. The Nazis must be driven out of the city and out of Germany! The Fuehrer should be shot! On 7 September, decrees against hindering the war effort or criticizing the regime were put into effect. They carried an automatic death penalty. The following months saw scores of Berliners, condemned by the infamous Peoples' Court for the crime of speaking freely, beheaded by axing in central Berlin's Moabit Prison.

Open complaint stopped, and opposition was again forced underground. Now, as if hopelessly depressed by every aspect of life, Berliners attempted to escape mentally. Concerts and operas played to overflowing crowds, and the thirty-five theatres and review palaces of the city were packed at every performance. Significantly, one of the most popular playwrights was

George Bernard Shaw!

The 400 motion picture houses scattered throughout the city, by edict of Joseph Goebbels, showed nothing but comedies—and travelogues of South America. The latter were usually preceded by a short propaganda film which sometimes elicited boos and hisses from the more foolhardy patrons. Film censorship in Germany was ironclad, but there was one place in Berlin where all the banned pictures could be seen: Hitler's private theater in the new Reich Chancellery.

As Christmas of 1939 approached, Berliners had practically nothing about which to be cheerful. Severe clothes rationing had gone into effect on 11 November. There was a coal shortage in the city. And even the cherished old Christmas carols had been perverted by the Nazis: "Silent night, Holy night, All is calm, All is bright. Adolf Hitler is Germany's star, Showing us greatness and glory afar. Bringing us Germans the might!" It is little wonder that Berliners got drunker that New Year's Eve than they had ever gotten before.

During 1940, the city was constantly aflutter with hundreds of thousands of red and black swastika flags in celebration of Germany's military victories. Anyone who failed to put out a flag was given two hours' grace in which to buy one and get it on display. Failing to do so, he was immediately carted away.

The city's bells rang for three days following the capitulation of each of the invaded countries: Holland, Belgium, France, Denmark, Norway. There were silent belfries all over Berlin, however, which told a less optimistic story—their bells already had been melted down to meet shortages of metal for war production.

Nonetheless, by August of 1940, Adolf Hitler was so confident of conquering Great Britain that he ordered the construction of a reviewing stand on Pariserplatz, just east of the Brandenberg Gate and across from the famous Adlon Hotel. There he intended to watch his returning victorious legions goosestep down the *Unter den Linden*. But when British bombers attacked industrial North Berlin that same month (the first air attack upon the city), it became apparent that the English were not about to collapse—and the victory stand came down, and was put into storage along with Hitler's plans for invading the British Isles.

Reich Marshal Hermann Goering, commander of the Luftwaffe, had promised Berliners that if his air force let a single British bomb fall upon German soil they could call him "Herr Meyer." As the city's residents stumbled to their shelters on the night of 29 August, they cursed "Herr Meyer" almost as much as the British bombers.

Braving the dense Berlin flak, the English Lancasters flew in to bomb the central, or Mitte, district where the government buildings were clustered. Ten Berliners were killed in the raid, the first mortalities from Allied air attacks upon the city. During the four remaining months of 1940, the British made 28 night raids on Berlin. However, there were no accurate night bombsights at that time and after-dark bombing was an erratic affair. Too, the raiding missions usually were undertaken by few more than a dozen planes. As a consequence, bomb damage was negligible and only 515 Berliners were killed.

After each of these raids the curious population came out to watch the Fire Brigades, monster-like in their asbestos suits, fight conflagrations, or clustered around to observe the cleanup squads clearing debris away from some shattered building. Indeed, it was remarked among the inhabitants of the city that if the damage from any future air raids was no worse, there was little cause for worry about that particular manifestation of war.

Their optimism was ill-founded. By May, 1945, over 50,000 of the city's residents would lose their lives in the bombings, more than twice that number would be seriously injured, and 612,000 buildings would be totally destroyed. But during the years 1941 and 1942, the English would mount only small, harassing raids against the German capital as attention shifted to the campaigns in Greece and North Africa, where German forces went to the aid of the Italians.

When, in June of 1941, Hitler began Operation Barbarossa—a massive attack against Russia—pessimistic Berliners rushed to the city's bookstores for any volume dealing with Napoleon's disastrous Russian campaign 129 years earlier. Their pessimism deepened with the entrance of the United States into the war against the Axis powers in December of that year. Most Germans had great respect for America's entry into World War I which had turned the tide against Germany.

Still, in 1941-42, Berlin seemed to have been little touched physically by the war. Except for a few craters in the Tiergarten, the labor gangs had cleared away most of the evidence of bombing. (It was these gangs, made up of Jews and political prisoners, who had also been charged with the suicidal job of disarming unexploded aerial mines.) "Sweeping Gangs," young Jewish or half-Jewish girls, followed the cleanup crews with great twig brooms, sweeping up whatever litter was left. Devastated sites which could not be totally cleared were walled away from view by construction fences bearing the obligatory proclamation: "Thank the Fuhrer that we build here."

Berliners, thronging down the city's streets past shop windows filled with luxurious consumer goods, looked well dressed. But it was all illusion. The shops had nothing to sell; their show windows were kept decorated by government order. And the Berliners, wistfully studying the displays, were wearing the last of their prewar clothes. Apparel was in such short supply that even a pair of leather shoelaces cost $4.00 on the burgeoning black market. And before a Berliner could buy a new pair of shoes, a city inspector searched his home to verify the fact that he had no other usable pair. An increasing number of children began to be seen wearing the Hitler Youth uniform—it was far easier to get a new uniform from the government than it was to buy civilian clothing.

Most of the suits and dresses which Berliners wore now did not fit properly; everyone had lost weight because of the stringent food rationing. Berliners were always hungry, and for that reason food was their most constant topic of conversation. Except for a few places, like Horcher's where a Nazi VIP could still get a lavish meal for one hundred Deutsche marks, even the restaurants offered the meagerest of meals.

Almost as much as food, Berliners missed their liquor, beer, coffee, and cigarettes. Liquor had all but ceased to exist, and the beer and coffee were the worst possible ersatz. The cigarette ration, which had originally been six cigarettes a day for men, three for women, had now been cut to three a day for the men, with no allowance made for women.

Soap had long been in such short supply that subway stations and other cramped areas were permeated with body odors. Fortunately, it was something to which Berliners slowly became inured.

Most Berliners traveled by subway or on the elevated trains which continued to run with crack efficiency. Except for official cars and military vehicles, automobiles had disappeared from the streets. Taxicabs could be used only by official permit or for emergencies, and only twenty-five percent of the city's buses were still operating. Consequently, homebound workers had to battle for seats on all the available conveyances.

Tense, tired, and irritable, Berliners took to arguing over everything, fell to fighting at the least provocation. The rudeness, especially of shopkeepers, waiters, and public servants, became such a problem that Joseph Goebbels launched an intensive "politeness campaign." It had little effect. Berliners simply turned their invective against the Propaganda Ministry. Housewives took to cocking their ears toward their open garbage cans and proclaiming: "Listen! Doctor Goebbels is speaking."

Yet all of these changes in the city and in the lives of its people were insignificant compared to what was happening to Berlin's Jews. These were easily recognizable: they were more emaciated than the average Berliner, and far shabbier in dress. Their food rations allowed only for bread and spoiled vegetables, and, denied all but the most menial labor, they had little money with which to buy those. As if more pointed designation was needed, on 19 September 1941, it became mandatory for all Jews to wear the yellow Star of David over their left breasts.

No sooner had that law gone into effect than a massive roundup of Berlin Jews commenced, the third of a series of such "arrests" since 1938. With vague references about "deportation to the east," Jews were piled into cattle trains which left Berlin at night for occupied Poland.

Then, on 27 May, in the Prague suburb of Holesovice, the man responsible for directing the "final solution of the 'Jewish problem,'" Reinhard Heydrich, was assassinated. The entire Nazi hierarchy trembled with fear. It was thought that Heydrich's own SS had engineered the killing, and the Nazis became acutely aware of their own vulnerability. (The assassination actually was the work of two British-trained Czech agents.) In reprisal for Heydrich's death, Hitler ordered the entire populace of the town of Lidice, Czechoslovakia, executed.

On the day of Heydrich's death, a lesser but consequent act of defiance against the Nazis was made in

Berlin. An attempt was made to burn down a Propaganda Ministry exhibit, called the "Russian Paradise," which had opened in the *Lustgarten*—Berlin's huge square next to the *Kaiserschloss* in the center of the city.

The exhibit, an anti-Soviet display, was made up of such items as a Russian secret police house of torture and a squalid collection of filthy huts, supposedly removed right from the streets of Minsk. (When this part of the show was subsequently closed, a favorite joke making the rounds in Berlin was: Q. Why did they close the Soviet Paradise? A. Because the people in North Berlin wanted their things back.)

The fire bombing of the exhibit was the work of an underground organization known as the "Herbert Baum Group." When the Gestapo apprehended 14 of its members, Heinrich Himmler ordered them—along with 236 "Jews and Communists"—machine-gunned to death at the SS barracks in the South Berlin suburb of Gross Lichterfelde. The event was widely publicized as a warning to the numerous other anti-Nazi organizations in Berlin. But the warning had little effect, and underground groups continued their work.

One of the most dedicated was the "Uncle Emil Group" whose membership was drawn primarily from the artistic community of Berlin and whose efforts were directed toward aiding Jews and people who were "wanted" by the Gestapo. Another was the Kreisau Circle, led by Count Helmuth von Moltke. A tall, humorous, simplistic man, von Moltke devoted his energies to preparing for German rehabilitation once Hitler was destroyed. Rote Kapelle, on the other hand, was an active intelligence cell that took its orders from Moscow, via its leader, Harro Schulze-Boysen, who worked for the Luftwaffe's intelligence service.

Werner Steinbrink organized university students of Berlin into an active group which circulated anti-Nazi literature. It was one of a number of youth groups, including many of the Hitler Youth, whose work against the regime became so plaguing that the Nazis established a special concentration camp for teenagers in the Rhineland. Students, churchmen, labor groups, artists, people in all professions and from every strata of society in Berlin banded together wherever possible to carry on the struggle against Hitler.

When the German armies began to suffer a series of defeats, beginning with the British offensive at El Alemain in October of 1942, it seemed possible that the position of the resistance groups might be strengthened. But, though these defeats caused general opposition to the war to flare up again, they increased the fanaticism within the Nazi ranks to such an extent that resistance activities were made even more difficult and dangerous.

In November of 1942, American troops landed in Africa. By May of the following year, the entire Afrika Korps had surrendered. Meanwhile, General Friedrich von Paulus' German Sixth Army, trapped in Stalingrad, surrendered to the Soviets on 31 January 1943.

For the better part of a year, news from the Russian front had been bad. Berliners had watched the ever lengthening hospital trains rolling into their city at night, had seen their 116 hospitals filling with wounded from the Russian campaign. Yet, on Saturday, February 6, when they were told of the Stalingrad defeat, that 280,000 men would not be returning home, Berliners were stunned. Within hours the Shrine of the Unknown Soldier on *Unter den Linden* was covered with thousands of fresh flowers, and black was the most common dress in the city.

The mourning did not stop with the news of Stalingrad. In Berlin itself there were more deaths for which to grieve. In a final vicious blow against the Jews, the Nazis decreed that the Jews of the city must be re-

Hitler with admirers. (UPI)

moved by the Fuhrer's birthday, 20 April 1943. A massive wave of arrests took place. Jews were dragged from the streets and thrown into waiting vans. Ubiquitous Blockleiters reported suspected hiding places to the SS Lightning Squads.

By now, most Berliners knew—if only by rumor—the fate awaiting the Jews. As they had in previous Jewish roundups, many Berliners showed in every possible way their disapproval of the treatment of the Jews. Crowds gathered at the Race Research Office to try to convince officials that Jewish friends were really "Aryan"; thousands of people physically attempted to prevent the arrest of Jewish neighbors. At one large building on the Rosenstrasse where Jews were being held awaiting shipment to concentration camps, 6,000 women marched in protest until the prisoners were released. In most instances, however, the unarmed civilians were helpless before the armed SS troops, and the loaded boxcars continued to leave Berlin for Polish concentration camps.

With the British air raid on the night of March 1-2, terror was added to the despair of the Berliners. This was the largest raid that had so far been mounted by the British. Dropping their eerie red marking flares with uncanny accuracy, the English bombardiers wreaked havoc on the western and southern districts of Berlin, including the fashionable suburbs of Dahlem and Wannsee where many of the top Nazis lived.

Overnight Berlin became a war-ravaged city. More than 100,000 people were made homeless and wandered the streets in shock, carrying with them only the few personal possessions they had been able to salvage. Damage was so extensive that repair was impossible. Entire blocks of rubble were simply roped off. Ominous signs appeared on black and red striped barriers, warning of unexploded aerial mines: "Achtung! Minen!" Incendiaries created thousands of fires which sent thick, black columns of smoke into the morning sky. On some streets the asphalt, heated by the fires, was too hot to walk upon, and phosphorous bombs would continue to ignite throughout the city during the whole of the following week.

In a series of day and night bombings of Hamburg in late July, British and American raiders almost leveled that city. As trainloads of refugees poured into Berlin with stories of the attacks and of Hamburg's devastation, Goebbels urged that ". . . every individual who is not obligated . . . to stay in Berlin . . . move to regions less subject to air attack." As if to add leverage to the propaganda minister's efforts at civilian evacuation, British planes dropped leaflets warning that the bombing of Berlin would be the sequel to Hamburg.

Thrown into near panic, people by the thousands began to flee the city. Railroad stations were jammed and every train leaving Berlin—whether going north, east, south, or west—was packed to overflowing. After a few days, however, the exodus tapered off and at the end of August nearly 3,000,000 Berliners still remained.

In the next months, the German capital suffered almost continuous bombardment by the Allies. A single raid in November of 1943 completely leveled one thousand acres of the city. The number of people left homeless by the devastation was staggering. Rooms were requisitioned for the bombing victims. But this meant lodging total strangers together in cramped and crowded quarters. It meant, also, the separation of families, and difficult emotional adjustments for people whose nerves already were at the breaking point.

No wonder that many of the citizens chose to live amid the rubble ruins of their former homes, or to build makeshift shacks of whatever material scraps they could find. A series of "shantytowns" sprang up around the perimeter of the capital, and signs rose from rubble mounds: "Don't remove rubble. This is still our home."

Yet, with all this, there was a strange atmosphere of normalcy about the city: subways and elevated trains continued to run. Mail was delivered on schedule, and the telephone exchanges in all parts of Berlin functioned efficiently. Newspapers appeared regularly at kiosks and on the doorsteps of subscribers. Motion picture houses and theaters were well patronized. White-coated Schupos still were stationed at traffic intersections, and the corner flower women continued to hawk their wares with traditionally acidic humor.

But the ravages of war were lined deeply into the tired, gray faces of the people of Berlin. Mortally weary from nights on end of bomb-spawned insomnia, they fell asleep standing up in queue lines, on subways, wherever they stood still for more than a moment or two. The fatigue was particularly noticeable in the industrial workers, who now were putting in double shifts.

In August, 1943, thousands of workers went on strike. While not all of them were in any way associated with the anti-Nazi underground movement, many of them belonged to the "Robby Group," founded by Robert Uhrig. Joseph Goebbels authorized increased food rations as a work-return inducement, but defiantly they refused to resume work. Gestapo and SS were called in. At the Siemens Elecrical Works alone, six hundred workers were arrested. Mass arrests followed at Osram, Frigidaire, Ford, Borsig, and other industrial plants in Berlin.

Shortly after the Normandy invasion of 6 June 1944, rumors circulating among Berliners of a plot against Hitler's life by a group of Wehrmacht officers came to the attention of Heinrich Himmler. For some time, Himmler had been aware of the existence of a resistance group in the Wehrmacht, and had had a number of the ringleaders under surveillance. Two civilian members of the conspiracy, Adolph Reichwein and Julius Leber, were arrested early in July but, oddly, Himmler took no further steps against the conspirators.

The plotters, led by the famous General Ludwig Beck (who, when chief of the general staff in 1938, had attempted to organize a generals' coup against Hitler), included such well-known persons as Carl Goerdeler, former mayor of Leipzig; Field Marshal Erwin Rommel; Count Wolf von Helldorf, chief of the Berlin police force; and Colonel Count Clause von Stauffenberg.

On 20 July 1944, the young and handsome von Stauffenberg placed the bomb under Hitler's conference table at the Fuehrer's Headquarters in Rastenberg. East Prussia. Believing Hitler dead, von Stauffenberg rushed back to the headquarters of the Replacement Army on Bendlerstrasse in Berlin. There, he discovered that, because the co-conspirators had received word that Hitler had survived the assassination attempt, no action had been taken to put the prearranged take-over plans into effect. Stauffenberg immediately assumed command and sent out the necessary emergency orders to commanders throughout the Reich and in occupied territories.

Commandant of Berlin, General Paul von Hase, a party to the conspiracy, called on the guard battalion *Grossdeutschland* under Major Otto Remer to surround the government ministries and various key SS offices. Major Remer, though ignorant of the plot, acted upon these orders from his superior officer.

Goebbels, at his Propaganda Ministry, did not know that anything was amiss until late afternoon, when Hitler called to tell him of the bomb attempt. Major Remer, under orders from General von Hase to arrest Goebbels, confronted the propaganda minister but, after only a brief exchange of words, Goebbels succeeded in winning the major's support against the coup. This robbed the conspirators of their own strength, particularly so because they had failed to use the available force of the Berlin police—a force which might have turned events in their favor.

Goebbels alerted the SS barracks at Gross Lichterfelde, where *Obersturmbannfuhrer* Otto Skorzeny rallied the disorganized troops. At 6:30 that evening, the propaganda minister broadcast the news of the failure of the attempt on the Fuehrer's life.

Having failed to secure control of the city of Berlin, the entire *Putsch* collapsed. Stauffenberg was executed that very night by a Nazi firing squad, the first of nearly 5,000 individuals implicated in the plot and summarily executed.

Most Berliners did not know that the coup had been attempted until they heard Goebbel's broadcast. For the next few days, as tanks stood protective guard over the government section of the city and Gestapo and SS units hunted down suspected "traitors," terror gripped the city.

Hitler used the assassination attempt as an opportunity to purge the Wehrmacht and destroy the last remnants of its independence. He proclaimed total war, and appointed Joseph Goebbels as plenipotentiary to organize "total mobilization." Now, with France and East Prussia fallen and Allied armies marching on the Fatherland, he was more determined than ever to sacrifice the entire German nation in his war. Following the disastrous Ardennes Offensive on the western front, which he personally commanded, Hitler returned to Berlin on 16 January 1945.

This city to which he came bore little resemblance to his prewar capital. Piles of rubble clogged the streets. Thousands of buildings had been leveled by aerial bombs, and hundreds of thousands were fire-gutted skeletons of brick and mortar. Partially damaged structures listed dangerously over streets and roadways, and white columns of rising dust marked the collapsing of endless buildings. Spirals of black smoke rose into the air from recent bomb strikes, spreading a thin film of oily soot over the city. The acrid taste and smell of old fires was in everyone's mouth and nostrils.

In marked contrast to the cramped, dank, foul-smelling shelters in which Berliners spent most of their hours, Hitler moved into a labyrinthian, air-conditioned, gourmet-stocked bunker (complete with garages, workshops, a hospital, a power plant, and a telephone exchange) fifty feet below the Chancellery garden. There, comfortably ensconced and in the company of his staff and a number of high ranking Nazi officials, he was totally oblivious to the suffering and devastation in the city above him.

Had there been any of the Fuehrer's conferees concerned with, or bold enough to mention to him, the untold miseries being forced upon the civilian population, in all likelihood he would have screamed the person to silence—as he had General Alfred Jodl on another occasion—with the words: ". . . spare me the trivial things!"

The trivialities? Men, women, and children standing in muted shock at the edges of thirty-foot craters and around demolished buildings waiting for loved ones to be dug out. Thousands of twelve and thirteen year old boys being marched to the front, many without either guns or ammunition, to form a human wall of corpses against Russian tanks.

The coffin lending services at cemeteries where, because of the heavy death toll, the few tarred wooden coffins available were used only for formal funeral services. Those finished, and the mourners gone, bodies were dumped into their graves and the caskets made ready for the next renters.

The refugee trains rolling slowly and endlessly into Berlin from the east, fleeing from the three Soviet

Hitler saluting a battalion of labor corps. (UPI)

Hitler at an anniversary of the "Beer Hall Putsch." (UPI)

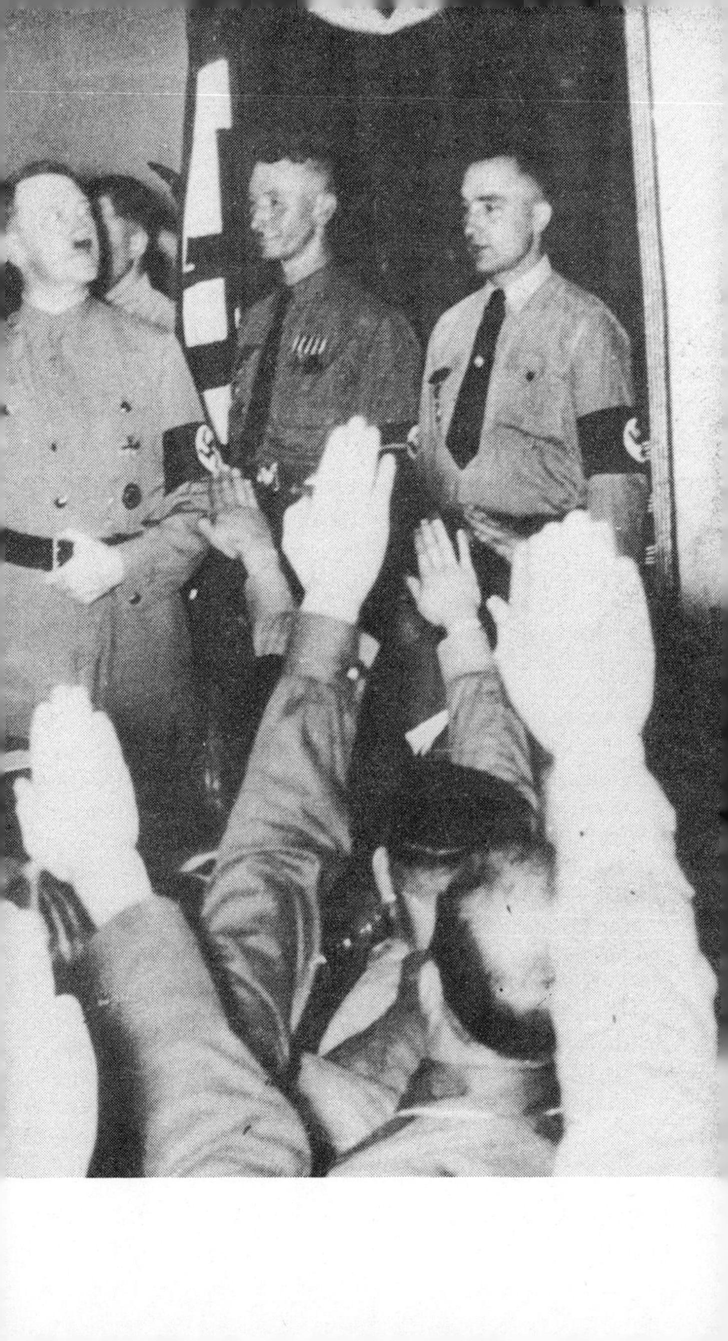

Army Groups moving relentlessly across western Poland into Silesia and Pomerania. One, an open coal car, held hundreds of Silesian children, packed so closely together that they had to stand without moving during the four-day journey through seventeen-below zero temperatures. (Most of them were frozen to death long before the train reached its destination.)

On 27 January forward units of the first Belorussian Army reached a point along the Oder River, one-hundred miles from Berlin. During February, two and one-half million Soviet soldiers moved up all along the Oder-Neisse line and stood ready to launch their final attack upon Berlin.

While Berliners looked desperately to the west for the Allies to save them from a brutal Russian conquest, Hitler sat in his bunker concocting a series of fantasies about the impregnability of the German capital, exhorting his depleted armies to fight to the last man, and proclaiming that if the war was lost, the nation should perish for ". . . those who remain after the last battle will be only the inferior ones, all the good ones will have been killed."

At 10:50 p.m., on the night of April 30, 1945—seven hours after Adolf Hitler had shot himself to death—Sergeants Egorov and Kantariya unfurled Red Banner number five of the Third Soviet Shock Army from the dome of the pitted, blackened Reichstag. The most symbolically important building in the capital of the Third Reich had fallen to the victorious Russians. The battle for Berlin had begun along the banks of the Oder River, 48 miles from the city, 14 days earlier, on April 16. Behind the Oder-Neisse line, the Soviet armies had spent more than two months preparing for this final battle. When forward units of Marshal Georgi Zhukov's First Belorussian Army reached the Oder River on January 27 of 1945, rumors of imminent Russian conquest spread throughout the city followed by panic when the Berlin police donned helmets and began to carry rifles later in February. When it became apparent that the Russian advance had halted, many Berliners turned to the outlawed BBC broadcasts for news of the approaching Anglo-American armies, looking hopefully to them as the city's savior from the Russians and the fanatical Nazis.

Georgi Zhukov, the short, thickset professional soldier whose career had begun in the Czarist cavalry, was anxious to press his advantage over the Germans. On February 4, he reported to Joseph Stalin, who was in Yalta meeting with Winston Churchill and Franklin D. Roosevelt, that he was planning to attack Berlin. At which Stalin snapped back, "Don't waste your time! Dig in . . ."

For the troops of the First Belorussian Army, the delay would hold one unexpected advantage. On April 5, Adolf Hitler, in the illogical belief that Prague was the real target of the Russians, ordered four units of Army Group Vistula's best panzers south to reenforce Field Marshal Ferdinand Schoerner's defense of the Czechoslovakian capital.

But the Germans also gained from the Soviet delay. The spring thaw melted much of the river ice that could have facilitated a Soviet crossing. More important, the Germans were given a respite in which to reorganize their retreating armies and establish defenses.

Along the west bank of the Oder River, the Germans built their first lines of defense—trenches, bunkers, barbed wire, and minefields in a belt which varied in depth from one to five miles. Approximately ten miles in back of these fortifications were a series of non-continuous trenches. At various distances behind these were some crude tank traps, barriers, and a few entrenched strong points. The next lines of defense were in the city of Berlin itself, with the first barrier constructed around the city limits.

Even using the extensive lake and canal system around the city, the sixty-mile circumference still required thousands of man-made barriers, only a small fraction of which had been completed. Too, this "Berlin Ring" required ten divisions of men, and the only soldiers available to the city's commandant, Lieutenant General Helmuth Reymann, were two infantry battalions, several engineer units, and thirty Peoples' Army battalions which were short of arms, training, and leadership.

Halfway into the city was a second line of defense, utilizing the Ringbahn, Berlin's circular railway system. Beyond this lay the Mitte District, the center of Berlin, where most of the important government buildings were located, including Adolf Hitler's bunker beneath the Reich Chancellery. This inner ring of defense was known as the "Citadel."

The "Citadel," with several thousand crack SS troops, was under the command of SS General Mohnke. Mohnke, charged with the defense of the Chancellery and the protection of the Fuehrer, would witness the last moments of both Adolf Hitler and Joseph Goebbels, order the firing of the Fuehrerbunker, and, on the night of April 30, 1945, make good his escape from beleaguered Berlin.

When Reymann, who was directly responsible to Hitler, met with the Fuehrer the first of March (it would be the only meeting between them), the Fuehrer was so preoccupied with mouthing empty and grandiose generalities about the city's defense that he failed to give Reymann either briefing or instructions. So it was that Berlin's only real hope was vested in the German Army Group Vistula facing the Russians across the Oder.

Army Group Vistula was commanded by the brilliant defensive strategist, Colonel General Gotthard Heinrici, a small man with simple ways and a rugged stamina. Army Group Vistula consisted of two armies—The Ninth Army and the Third Panzer Army. The Ninth was commanded by General Theodor Busse, the Third Panzer by Baron General Hasso von Manteuffel, an expert in armor tactics who had led the Ardennes Offensive. This army group, together with the Fourth Panzer Army to the south, represented the total German Army standing between the Russians and Berlin, a quarter of a million men, many of them unseasoned soldiers.

Against this depleted and pitiful force were massed two-and-a-half million Krasnoarmeyets (Red Army men). These Soviet troops were divided into three armies—the Second Belorussian Army under Marshal Konstantin Rokossovskii along the northern Oder, the First Belorussian Army of Marshal Georgi Zhukov directly east of Berlin, and the First Ukranian Army under the command of Marshal Ivan Konev, a big man whose broad, pleasant face belied his toughness.

The First Belorussian and the First Ukranian armies initiated the Battle for Berlin on the morning of April 16, starting their attacks at four and six a.m. respectively (Marshal Rokossovskii's Second Belorussian would not join the attack until the twentieth). Synchronized as closely as possible, the opening barrage by 41,000 cannons, mortars, and rocket launchers was an awesome display without parallel in military history. But the destructive effects were less than expected, for Heinrici, sensing the approaching onslaught, had shrewdly withdrawn his troops from the front line to wait out the cannonading in secondary entrenchments.

In order to help their engineers breach the Oder-Neisse rivers, Konev had Russian planes lay down a thick blanket of smoke along the river, while Georgi Zhukov resorted to a more bizarre scheme—batteries of blinding anti-aircraft searchlights beamed across the river in order to blind the enemy.

Konev bridged the Neisse River quickly, but Zhukov had trouble against General Karl Weidling's Fifty-Sixth Panzer Corps, despite the fact that the First Belorussians already had a major bridgehead at Kustrin prior to the attack. While Konev's forces gained ten miles in eight hours, Marshal Georgi Zhukov's first units, under the leadership of "the hero of Stalingrad," Colonel General Vasili Chuikov, were bogged down by the stiff resistance of the German Fifty-Sixth on Seelow Heights.

Konev was so successful that he called Stalin on the seventeenth for permission to turn his right flank and move on Berlin—an objective reserved originally for his rival, Zhukov. Stalin granted Konev's request. Having had little trouble penetrating the German Fourth Army, Konev—on the morning of the eighteenth—was pushing his troops northwest for Berlin.

Meanwhile, following the capture of Seelow Heights (Zhukov's furious anger at the slow progress of his Eighth Guard Army served to spur them to take the Heights during the night of the seventeenth and the early morning of the eighteenth), Zhukov's forces began to speed forward, driving a wedge between the German Fifty-Sixth Panzer Corps and the Ninth Army.

The Soviets had breached the German line in a number of places, the largest holes being those punched between the Fourth Army under Field Marshal Schoerner in the south and Busse's Ninth Army (part of Army Group Vistula) east of Berlin—and between the Ninth Army and the rest of Group Vistula to the north.

In an attempt to block these Russian invasion routes, the Fuehrer ordered Heinrici to attack south, Schoerner to attack north. But the task was beyond the greatly outnumbered and poorly supplied German troops. Schoerner's Fourth Army had been so badly mauled by Konev that it was unable to attack. And Heinrici, realizing that in order to save Army Group Vistula he must withdraw and regroup, chose to ignore Hitler's directive. He ordered the Ninth Army to withdraw, but General Busse refused, unwilling to defy Hitler's command to "stand fast."

In heavy fighting that day, the left (northern) wing of Busse's Army was turned and the Ninth began its slow retreat southwest, unable to fall back toward the city itself. In an irresistible display of strength, the First Belorussian Army was peeling the German defenders away from Berlin. While Busse's army was being pushed to the southwest, von Manteuffel's Third Panzer Army to the north was waiting to receive the shock of Marshal Rokossovskii's delayed attack. At the same time, Konev's Army was approaching the German Ninth Army from the south.

The only effective force which now stood between Zhukov and Berlin was Weidling's Fifty-Sixth Panzer Corps. The SS Nordland Division and the Eighteenth Panzer Grenadier Division were rushed forward to bolster it, but they only reached the front in time to join the Fifty-Sixth's retreat.

All of the attacking Russian armies advanced on 19 April, and some of the lead units came within sight of the outskirts of the German capital.

It was a quiet day in the city, ominously quiet. Goebbels gave his last speech on Radio Berlin, exhorting the citizens to "repulse the Mongolian hoards." Against a backdrop of eerie silence, the speech of the propaganda minister seemed louder than usual. More exhortations were to appear the next day in the special edition of the morning paper honoring the Fuehrer's fifty-sixth birthday.

Hitler celebrated the day in the Fuehrerbunker frantically issuing orders to his ministers and commanders. With him were Hermann Goering; Joseph Goebbels; Heinrich Himmler, the Reichsfuehrer SS; Joachim von Ribbentrop, the Foreign Minister for the Reich; Deputy Party Leader Martin Bormann; Albert Speer; and members of the general staff—Grand Admiral Karl Doenitz, Field Marshal Wilhelm Keitel, Colonel General Alfred Jodl, and Lieutenant General Hans Krebs.

Following the celebration—during which the Fuehrer assured the gathering of Nazi "Old Guard" that the Bolsheviks were about to suffer "their bloodiest defeat of all before Berlin"—most of the celebrants fled the city, anxious to get out before it became another of the Fuehrer's doomed "fortresses." The concept of the *festung*, or fortress, had always been one of Hitler's favorites. And he had thrown away hundreds of thousands of topflight troops by forcing them to defend cities which were impossible to relieve.

On 20 April, the birthday of the Fuehrer, Fortress Berlin became a closed city. No trains moved in or out. Postal and telegraph services, carried on with dogged regularity until now, ceased. Army trucks and cars moved eastward through confused groups of people with white, strained faces fleeing toward the western suburbs.

The anxious exodus of citizens was prompted by the first shelling of the capital by the Russians. Inured as the Berliners were to Allied bombings, the whistling shrieks of artillery shells were new and terrifying. It announced with unmistakable certainty that the Russians stood at the very threshold of the city. Yet almost at the moment that the Russians opened their attack upon Berlin itself, Hitler, still stubbornly refusing to look at the real situation, was demanding that the Oder front be held—a front which, except in the north, had for all realistic purposes fallen three days earlier!

The next day, Saturday the twenty-first, Russian dive bombers flew missions against the center of the capital, and Soviet artillery zeroed in on the government section. Hitler, when he heard the shelling, remarked, "It must be eight-inch guns firing from the Weissensee District."

His estimate was accurate. The Russians had reached the outskirts of that northeastern suburb, a workers' district with the strongest communistic sympathies in all of Berlin, where Soviet troops were being welcomed as liberators. The city's defensive ring had now been broken from the Koepenick section in the southeast to Weissensee in the northeast, and Soviet troops were moving down the Prenzlauer Alle, the boulevard leading from the northeastern corner of the city to the Alexander Platz—a prime objective for the advancing Russians not only because it was an important intersection, but also because the hated Gestapo had its headquarters there. To bolster the SS troops guarding that vital intersection, Hitler ordered a part of his personal bodyguard unit to the Alexander Platz.

It was on this day, too, that the Fuehrer organized 500 Chancellery personnel into a *Volkssturm* unit and that all ten-year-olds were inducted into the Hitler Youth. The leaders of the Third Reich were demonstrating total desperation in their orders and acts. Had they not been, in effect, death sentences for thousands, they would have been comically ridiculous.

Despite moments of euphoric hope, both Hitler and Goebbels recognized defeat. As early as April 2, Hitler had said that, though the Third Reich was overthrown, Germany must go on fighting to the very end. And, closing his speech to his Propaganda Ministry staff on April 21, Goebbels had shouted angrily: "All the plans, all the ideas of National Socialism are too high, too noble for such a (German) people . . . They deserve the fate that will now descend upon them!"

There was no doubt of the people's fate now. The Ninth German Army (the army which was to have held out against the Russians ". . . until the British kick us in the ass!" as Busse put it) was surrounded and fighting for its existence, and the Third Panzer Army was being pushed northeast. Nothing stood between the Russian armies and the people of Berlin except the Fifty-Sixth Panzer Corps and the units within the Berlin Defense Command.

That evening, as Hitler shuffled and reshuffled his tactical maps, he suddenly was elated to rediscover Group Steiner on the southern flank of the Third Panzer Army. He would send Group Steiner to attack south across the Russian front (already penetrating the Berlin suburbs) and block the Soviet advance! He called Steiner to promise him reenforcements for the attack, but neglected to tell the SS General just where this attack was supposed to take place.

Most Berliners had given up all hope of an Anglo-American rescue, or of a successful German defense. They simply waited for the end to come, concerned only with staying alive. They fought for places in queue lines waiting to draw pails of chlorinated water from public pumps, and spent hours cooking their meager rations over the minute and flickering flames of their gas burners (It was on the twenty-second that cooking with electricity became a crime punishable by death).

For many Berliners there was a real meal to be prepared on this day, for a special food ration was issued providing for one pound of meat, 250 grams of rice or oats, 250 grams of lentils, groats or beans, two pounds of sugar, 100 grams of ersatz coffee, some fat, and one can of vegetables or fruit. The queues lined up in front of food stores that Sunday were enormous, sometimes four abreast and several blocks long. While some people hoarded these "advance rations," eating sparingly to make the food last as long as possible, others consumed everything in what they thought of as "one last meal."

And well they might think after that fashion. Stacks of corpses were piled in the streets. Each day as the Russians came closer and closer, suicides increased.

And, all over the city, there appeared with increasing frequency a sickeningly gruesome sight—bodies dangling by the necks from lampposts and trees. Most of these were army deserters, though some were indiscreet individuals who had voiced anti-Nazi sentiments to the wrong person. Signs pinned to the corpses warned: "This is the fate of a deserter!" "I betrayed the Fatherland!" Flying courts-martial were permanently convened now and squads roamed the city dispensing instant "justice."

The bodies swinging ominously above sidewalk and street were calculated to threaten Berliners—either fight the Russians or be killed by the Nazis. But, as they had done in the past, most of the city's dwellers turned their backs upon the Nazis. Store windows and brick walls throughout Berlin carried a one-word admonition: "NEIN!" Its meaning was clear. The Berliners refused to defend the city for the Nazis.

At Hitler's conference with Keitel and Jodl at 5:30 on the evening of 22 April, the Fuehrer seemed on the verge of a total breakdown. He shrieked and raged because there had been no news of Steiner's attack—an attack which never took place, could not take place—but in a relatively rational moment admitted, "It's all lost!"

The Russian advance into the eastern suburbs had in no way been stemmed. Furthermore, German troops from northern Berlin had been sent to bolster the immobile Group Steiner, allowing Russian columns in the north to turn upon the city in an enveloping movement. Elements of Zhukov's army swept through Henningsdorf and encircled the northern suburb of Tegal. With Soviet forces at the eastern and northern edges of the city, with Red units racing up from the south, and with encirclement imminent, it was obvious that Berlin was doomed.

Himmler and von Ribbentrop both called the

Berlin, 1945. (UPI)

Fuehrerbunker, trying to persuade Hitler to leave the city while there was still time. He refused. But Keitel and Jodl, attempting to keep the military command intact as long as possible, prepared to move their headquarters to the southwest of Berlin outside of Potsdam.

In the midst of this mood of defeat and flight, a "final chance" presented itself to the desperate Nazi hierarchy. This "chance" was predicated on the supposition that von Ribbentrop would be able to arrange favorable peace terms if Berlin could only hold out for a while. With this in mind, Hitler and his staff proposed to turn General Walter Wenck's Twelfth Army (which was facing the Anglo-Americans across the Elbe) and rush them to Berlin to stand off the Russians. The Twelfth Army consisted of only two corps, the Forty-First Tank Corps and the Twentieth Army Corps, both of which were short of men and equipment, and were spread thinly along a front more than 100 miles long.

General Wenck, on his own initiative, had faced his army about to the east in preparation for defending the area against the Soviets. More particularly, he was determined to protect it from the fanatical Nazis attempting to carry out Hitler's "scorched earth" orders, and to provide an area of refuge for the hundreds of thousands of civilians who had swarmed into the region in an effort to escape the Russians.

The "scorched earth" order had been issued on 19 March, over the protestations of Reich Minister of Armament and War Production Albert Speer. This order specified that all industrial plants, bridges, railway and communication installations, electric facilities, waterworks, gasworks, waterways, ships, railcars, and food and clothing stores were to be destroyed, regardless of the life-needs of the people.

Speer was the only Reichminister who dared to tell the Fuehrer stark truths. Since October, 1944, he had waged an unsuccessful campaign to convince Hitler that the war should be ended. With the Russian capture of Silesia in January, the mines supplying sixty percent of Germany's coal were gone. Speer, the pragmatist, told Hitler, "The war is lost!" It was such honesty that prompted Hitler to say: "I don't want to see Speer alone anymore. He always has something unpleasant to tell me, and I can't bear that."

Finally giving up all hope of reasoning with Hitler, Speer decided to "eliminate" him by flooding the Fuehrerbunker with poison gas. However, this scheme proved unfeasible because Hitler, anticipating just such a possibility, had had the ventilation system adequately protected. In a last desperate effort to save Germany from the scorched earth policy, Speer than sought to induce key military and civilian commanders to sabotage the order. He found strong support in many quarters, but got a disheartening rebuff from General Reymann, the commandant of Berlin, who later said, ". . . as a soldier, I had to carry out orders . . . it was my duty to obey."

A direct contrast to General Reymann was the independent General Wenck. When Field Marshal Keitel personally delivered Hitler's order for the Twelfth Army to come to the relief of Berlin, Wenck accepted it with a promise to "attack eastward." With his small force, Wenck knew that it would be impossible for him to relieve Berlin. But he knew, also, that there was no use trying to reason with Keitel. Wenck simply planned to alter the orders slightly!

This alteration entailed driving his Twelfth Army south of Berlin to where the Ninth Army was trapped, and bringing that beleaguered force—and the refugees caught in the center of its encirclement—to the safety of the west.

Monday, 23 April was a clear, warm spring day. Lilacs and crocuses were blooming, and the scent of flowers and rain-soaked grasses mingled with the acrid

The dome of the Cathedral of Berlin after the fall. (UPI)

Direct fire from the Russians destroyed the Reichstag Building. (UPI)

odors of war. For the Berliners, a new hope bloomed, too, that day. Rumors spread through the city that a strong German army was coming from the west to defend it. The rumors were based on the Twelfth Army's turnabout, and were given added weight by the Nazis' trick of marching Berlin *Volkssturm* units eastward across the city to give the appearance of army units coming from the west. As with most rumors, this one had various versions, including the one that claimed Germany had made peace with the Anglo-Americans and that the army rushing to Berlin's defense was Army Group B—twenty divisions strong—which had surrendered to the Allies in the Ruhr basin five days earlier.

To the Berliners living in the west and northwest sections of the city the rumors were meaningless. Soviet forces already were battling in the western suburb of Pichelsdorf and would soon secure the Gatow and Staaken airdromes, as well as the Heerstrasse, an important access route into central Berlin.

Nor could dwellers in the southern suburbs take much comfort from the rumors as Konev's forces approached. Their "defenders" presented a heartbreaking sight: dirty, exhausted soldiers—often walking, wounded, wearing filthy, blood-soaked bandages—and frightened boys, their smooth faces almost hidden by large, steel helmets.

Furthermore, if the rumors were true, why were they being bombarded with propaganda leaflets calling all citizens to arms and announcing that the Fuehrer himself was assuming command of the Berlin area? General Reymann had been relieved as commander of Berlin that morning and had been put in charge of the Potsdam garrison. Colonel Kaether had replaced him in Berlin.

While some of the city's population took heart, most Berliners found little comfort in rumors, slogans, or the

Fuehrer's leadership. Refugees continued to stream out of the city heading west and southwest. For those who remained, the night seemed calm. There was only light bombing and a little flak.

But if that Monday was a day of relative peace, the day which followed, Tuesday the twenty-fourth, was a day of terror. The Soviets, well entrenched now in many of the suburbs, had brought up great quantities of artillery. On the twenty-fourth they unleashed a concerted barrage upon the center of Berlin from batteries encircling the city. The shelling lasted an hour. When it was finished, Russian troops began their final advance.

During that time, soldiers of Konev's First Ukranian Army had reached Potsdam, sixteen miles southwest of Berlin, and surrounded that outpost. Southwest of Berlin, Wenck's Twelfth Army, moving toward the rescue of Busse's Ninth Army, found itself engaged in heavy fighting as it collided with Konev's advancing Ukranians. Outside of Potsdam, Konev's Army also met friendly forces—Zhukov's First Belorussians coming around Berlin from the north.

Berlin was encircled. The last direct communication between Berlin and the outside world ended that night as the Nazi shortwave radio went off the air. A girl announcer, discarding the customarily compulsory "Heil Hitler" closing salutation, said quietly, "Good night. Good night, everybody."

Undoubtedly, the worst fighting in the Battle of Berlin took place in the next five days. The defense of the suburbs had fallen in large part to the *Volkssturm*. The trained Soviet soldiers had little difficulty overwhelming or frightening these young boys and old men into surrender. The main resistance came from the Fifty-sixth Panzer Corps who were falling back through the suburbs and fighting a rearguard action.

But as the Russians moved toward the downtown

A Berlin apartment building three years after the war. (UPI)

АЭРОПОРТ

area, they found themselves pitted against the last corps of fanatical SS soldiers. These were men whose only choice was to fight savagely, for capture by the Reds could mean only the most gruesome of fates. Almost all of them died in battle—"Faithful unto death."

The city was in chaos. In some districts the fighting was from building to building, as SS soldiers or Weidling's soldiers fell slowly back. Many Soviet commanders did not bother with the painstaking procedure of rooting out defenders holed-up in buildings; they simply razed the structure—or, in some instances, entire blocks—with tank fire, artillery, or demolition charges.

Fighting was hectic and confusing. German pockets of resistance were spotted throughout the city. Russians traveled through cellars in order to come up behind the German defenders, while the SS used the subway several times in order to surprise the Soviets from behind.

As the battle passed over them, Berliners were imprisoned in their shelters. Only the fact that their experiences were shared with so many others made their fearful panic bearable. Yet, as ominous as the sounds of battle had been, the silence which followed was worse. For it could only mean that that which they had most dreaded had come to pass—the Russians were taking the city.

As more and more of the city fell to the Soviet soldiers, the looting and raping and murdering began. Small comfort that the conquerors were somewhat less savage than they had been in their march through Poland and the eastern German provinces!

There is no way of knowing the number of sexual attacks made upon the girls and women of Berlin. It was common and it was wholesale. While revenge may have prompted some of the assaults the more probable cause of these widespread attacks was the fact that the wartime Soviet Army had permitted no leaves. There were hundreds of thousands of Red soldiers who had not even seen a woman for four years!

There was no planned campaign of terror against the civilian population. A rather poorly disciplined army of drafted rustics, fighting a long and bloody campaign, had conquered a large metropolitan city—what happened then was inevitable.

There are, however, conflicting accounts of what took place. In some areas of Berlin, the people considered the Soviet soldiers restrained, even courteous. In other sections, violent rapings, infanticides, and torture were reported. This disparity in conduct may be accounted for by the differences in the individuals making up the various units of the Russian army, as well as to the degree of control exercised over them by their officers.

From all accounts, the Mongolian soldiers were the most barbarous. These, of course, came from a culture which took for granted the right of the conqueror to enjoy the spoils of battle. But, no matter which the unit or what the culture of the Russian soldier, his command, "*Komm, Frau,*" could strike terror into a woman's heart.

Women disguised themselves to look deformed, pregnant, or hideously ugly. They hid in the debris of the city—more than one woman crawled to safety in an overturned bathtub, hundreds of which had been thrown into the streets by Russian soldiers who did not know what they were. There were some who found a Soviet officer to protect them, considering that "one" was better than "many." Others, less philosophical, committed suicide.

Suicides were common, particularly among the Nazis. And Adolf Hitler was contemplating his own end when, on the twenty-sixth he told Hanna Reitsch: "Death for me only means freedom from worries and a very difficult life."

Hanna Reitsch, the famous aviatrix, had flown into Berlin that day with General Ritter von Greim, commander of the Sixth Air Force at Munich. Theirs was to be the last German plane to land in the city. Von Greim had come to Berlin at Hitler's orders, to be promoted to chief of the Luftwaffe, replacing Goering who was under arrest at Berchtesgaden for attempt to depose Hitler. Yet even while the Fuehrer infected von Greim with patriotic zeal, another ferocious artillery barrage on the center of the city had begun. And, though Hitler could talk to von Greim of victory, defeat was certain.

Earlier, the Fuehrer had passed the command of Berlin to General Weidling. With the exception of the SS, his Fifty-sixth Panzer Corps was the only unit left which had any semblance of order. Now, the Russians were so close to the heart of the city that Weidling's headquarters were in the Anhalter Railway Station, just blocks south of the Fuehrerbunker.

While Russian shelling continued throughout the following day, Hitler's ridiculous orders streamed from the Fuehrerbunker. The Third Tank Army, the Ninth Army, the Twelfth Army must attack toward Berlin and recapture the city! (Fighting valiantly, the Ninth would break out of its encirclement, link up with Wenck's Twelfth on May 1, and, eluding Konev's First Ukranians, make a miraculous retreat to the Elbe River and surrender to the Americans.)

On that Saturday, 28 April, Hitler received two shattering pieces of news: the first, that Mussolini and his mistress, Clara Petacci, had been executed by Italian partisans; the second, reported by the BBC, that Himmler had made an offer of German surrender. Himmler's "treachery" threw Hitler into the most raging tantrum he had ever had.

The Soviets were now in the Citadel Section of Berlin. There, they ran into Mohnke's SS, who defended the area building by building. For the Nazis, surrounded in the center of the city, there was no place to withdraw, and death was only a matter of hours. The end of the Third Reich was at hand.

Adolf Hitler and Eva Braun, his bride of one day, committed suicide at 3:30 p.m., on 30 April, 1945. Their bodies were cremated in the garden of the Chancellery as Captain Stefan Noystroev's battalion was capturing the Reichstag in a room-by-room battle.

General Weidling, commandant of Berlin, surrendered the city on 2 May, two days after Hitler's suicide. Five days later, Germany surrendered unconditionally.

Berlin now was a vast pile of ruins, dubbed by the Russians as "the stone jungle," and by Harry Hopkins "the modern Carthage." Dust and ash cast a dirty fog over everything, and smoke issued from still smoldering fires. Once, in anger, Goebbels had shouted: ". . . when we step down, let the whole earth tremble." It was in Berlin that these fanatics had staged their Gotterdammerung . . . and the earth had trembled.

No Lack of Heroes

by Philip Finnley

*T*he past thousand years have seen much bloodshed in the land known as Vietnam. The people have fought for the existence of their culture and the enshrinement of that culture in their own free and independent state. They have produced many men willing to fight and to die for this goal, men no more nor less complex than our own heroes. The Vietnamese have perhaps produced more but only because they have had to. As Le Loi, the Vietnamese hero who defeated the armies of Imperial China, said of his country and countrymen:

"Our people long ago established Vietnam as an independent nation with its own customs and traditions, and these are different from those of the foreign country to the north [China]. We have sometimes been weak and sometimes powerful, but at no time have we suffered from a lack of heroes."

The diminutive people of Vietnam first declared their independence from China in the chaos brought about by the fall of the mighty T'ang dynasty in the tenth century. The last Chinese army was driven from Vietnamese soil in 1427. When they numbered no more than a million, the people defeated the armies of the Mongol Khan. After the French arrived, they fought them in small groups, in massive rebellion, and finally in full-scale modern warfare—and they defeated them. In their thousand years of warfare, the people and their heroes have fought much the same kind of war. They have given up their homes, their possessions, their cities, and their industry—and retreated to the country. They have never given up the land.

The culture for which they fought was a blend of many influences, the dominant being Chinese. The traditional Vietnamese state was much like that of China: a mandarinate staffed the administrative agencies of the throne and entrance to the elite was by examination. The emperor was a Confucian monarch, the father and mother of his people, who ruled by grace of the Mandate of Heaven.

The land that is Vietnam creates a slow curve bounded by the South China sea. When the French first came, it was known as the kingdom of Dai Viet. The modern name Vietnam was not adopted until the early nineteenth century. It means, in Vietnamese characters, the Chinese phrase "south of Yueh" (Yueh being the ancient name for the modern Chinese province of Kwangtung whose capital is Canton). The Chinese themselves knew the land as An Nam, "pacified south," and the French had their own name: Indochina. For the French, Indochina was divided into three areas: Cochin-China, the extreme south where they found the small mud village of Saigon; Annam, the central area and site of the royal city of Hue; Tongking, which borders China and holds the city of Hanoi.

The French first found this country in the seventeenth century when its culture and history had had centuries of development. But these first Frenchmen sought a single goal: the conversion of the heathen to the Christian religion, and the land was to them only a repository of unsaved souls. In 1623, the man who launched France upon its eastern course of empire first arrived in Vietnam. He was Alexander of Rhodes, born in 1591 and a member of the Society of Jesus.

Alexander was to spend twenty-five years in the Far East, much of it in the unexplored interior, preaching to the people. But he often encountered the antipathy of the elite, which considered Christianity a strange heresy, and finally Alexander was captured and sentenced to death. The punishment was later changed to perpetual banishment and Alexander left to begin an even greater task of conversion.

To seventeenth century Europe, Asia and in particular Vietnam were uncharted spots on a map. Traders had come and gone but few expressed an interest in the mysteries of the East. Alexander sought audience with the Pope and later convinced the College of Propaganda at Rome that the East was for Catholicism a land of little knowledge and much need. His requests were granted and in France he formed what was to be the great French missionary activity, the *Société des Missions Etrangères* (Society of Foreign Missions).

The first French were the traders of the French East India Company, sailing from French bases in India, and whose favor was secured with the government of France by liberal percentages paid directly to King Louis XIV. Even aided by priests who knew the area and the language, these efforts met the hostility of the Vietnamese and the resistance of Dutch and British traders. Despite such small successes as the establishment of a small trading base in Cochin-China in 1664-1665, they were largely unsuccessful.

The next opportunity the French had to enter Vietnam came in the 1780's when Pigneau de Behaine, consecrated Bishop of Adran and vicar apostolic to Cochin-China, met a young dissident Annamese prince on an island off the coast of Vietnam. Pigneau de Behaine promised the prince French aid in his efforts to topple the throne in return for concessions to the French. In 1787, Pigneau de Behaine returned to France where, as representative of the prince, he signed a mutual aid treaty. But when he returned to Vietnam the prince had already succeeded in his efforts and was now the emperor Gia Long. The treaty was never enacted.

French activity always depended upon conditions in the mother-country and now France was swept up in revolution. In the anti-religious fervor of the ruling committees the *Société des Missions Etrangères* was driven from the city and finally from the country. Its priests continued their preaching in distant Vietnam but a new Annamese king had eliminated almost all the French priests.

In the restoration which followed Napoleon, the *Société* returned to favor under the new Louis XVIII, King by Grace of God. A general upswing in religious fervor among the French was channeled by missionary groups; conversion of the natives now became part of the God-given historic role of the French people. At the same time, the bureaucrats of the French Ministry of the Marine and the officers of the professional navy came to support the missionaries. To these men, the missionaries were Frenchmen—Frenchmen gloriously showing the flag in a foreign land.

But French attention continued to languish until Louis Napoleon converted the French republic into an empire. He courted the religious party and this meant backing missionary activities in the Far East. Finally, responding to the suggestions of the first French minister to China, he seized news of the maltreatment of a

Spanish missionary to order a massive French mission to Vietnam. A fleet was gathered and arrived with fourteen ships of the line, two thousand French troops, four hundred and fifty Spanish troops, and several hundred Filipino Tagal mercenaries hired by the French. The mission was to seize the port of Tourane (modern Da Nang) and attack the city of Hue.

Tourane fell without resistance; the Vietnamese simply fell back into the thick jungle they knew so well. The French dug into the area around the port but while an Annamese army was near the scene, it refused to fight a decisive battle. Now the French felt the full fury of another Vietnamese weapon—the climate. Sanitation conditions, poor to begin with, deteriorated even more with the rains. Cholera and scurvy decimated the troops and with only a few battles fought, the French were soon unable to take any offensive operations.

Admiral Genouilly, the commander of the French forces, now attempted to win a consolation victory. Leaving a small force to guard Tourane, he set sail for the small mud-hut village of Saigon which was open to attack from the sea. Fighting lasted for eight days and the French took the city and with its supplies of arms, powder, and rice. But typhus broke out among the troops. Admiral Genouilly wrote of his command: "Everything here tends towards ruin, men and things."

In late 1859 Admiral Genouilly was replaced and by March of 1860 French troops had left Tourane while still holding Saigon. In France powerful elements in the Ministry of Marine and Colonies continued to push the enterprise and in June, 1862, King Tu-Duc of Annam made peace.

Tu-Duc was half-mad and anti-foreign; he had met the French invasion by ignoring it. But the French had denied him the rice from the rich areas of Cochin-China and now insurrection had broken out in northern Tongking. The resulting treaty granted France an indemnity, ceded three ports, and provided that Annam could no longer grant any of its land to any other foreign power without the approval of Paris. Despite Annamese efforts to break the treaty, ratifications were exchanged on April 14, 1863.

With the outbreak of the Franco-German war of 1871, a new group of men arose in France. They were the colonialists, whose imperialist credentials were impeccable, and who fused the roles of missionary, trader, and patriot. For France they proposed a new role: bringing civilization to the backward natives. They expounded wild schemes based upon exploratory missions into Vietnam: new and better trade routes were available if Vietnam was a colony, and these routes would transform Saigon into a commercial center which would eclipse Shanghai.

The prototype of these new men was Francis Garnier, naval lieutenant, and Inspector of Indigenous Affairs, who led the first of a series of quasi-scientific expeditions in northern Vietnam and published his report in 1873. He became involved in an unofficial plot to capture the city of Hanoi and present it to the government. Visiting the city with a small band of men he declared it in a state of anarchy and proceeded to forcibly expel the troops of the king. With sixty men he seized the city's citadel but was killed repulsing an attack of Vietnamese pirates. Garnier died in what the representative of official France called "odious aggression" but he also died on the barricades showing the French flag and for this he was called a hero.

France was now a republic, a republic of the trader and the merchant, but it found itself confronted on the continent by the power of a growing Germany under Bismarck. Its attention once more turned East and was inspired by the opportunity for commercial success. Men such as Chasseloup-Laubat, the former Minister of Marine and Colonies, headed up and found support in the academic community of France. Geographical societies sprung up all over France and all stressed what science had supposedly shown: that incredibly lucrative and untapped resources awaited France in Vietnam. In 1882, Professor Paul Gaffarel, founder of the Dijon Geographical Society, expressed the view of the day:

"The future is in the Far East. There is no doubt about it. It would be better to renounce every idea of European annexation, and to shift our field of action to the Far East. The natives are children who are just being admitted to civilization. Is it not our duty to direct them, to instruct them, to educate them morally?"

In 1880, the Third French Republic held an overseas empire of almost a million square miles. But within five years, by 1885, the area had grown to over three million square miles and Frenchmen ruled Africa to Asia. The man who constructed this empire was Jules Ferry, Premier of France. In 1881 Ferry turned his attention toward Vietnam.

Since 1874, France had controlled the foreign affairs of Annam under the treaty of that year, but the matter was clouded by China's continued claims to sovereignty and Annamese king Tu-Duc's efforts to play the French off against the Chinese by continuing to send tributary to Peking. France had direct control over southern Cochin-China, the middle of the country was the independent kingdom of Annam, and the northern Tongking was under Annam's jurisdiction.

French expeditions were sent north supposedly to clear the Red River of pirates, and in late 1880, one such mission was dispatched with its true aim to occupy Hue and Tongking. Surprising the French, the Chinese, at the invitation of Tu-Duc, moved their troops in. With the French facing the Chinese in Tongking, the issue was unresolved with the downfall of Ferry's first ministry in 1881.

When Ferry returned to office in 1883, French troops in the north were fighting the Black Flag, local troops connected with the royal court at Hue. Ferry now stood ready to establish a protectorate over the whole of Vietnam and was given the chance when Tu-Duc was poisoned at his court by a rival faction. The French fully exploited the advantage, rushed five thousand troops, and, after a brief bombardment of Hue, forced the new king Disiep-Hoa to sign a treaty giving France outright control of Tongking and right to unreserved military, political, and financial intervention in Annam.

While Chinese troops continued activity in Tongking, and the Chinese government still claimed the state, northerners like Li Hung-chang were unwilling to commit their armies to fight in the extreme south. Chinese policy wavered and finally collapsed. On June 6, 1884, the Treaty of Hue was signed and the French began an era of colonial mastership in Vietnam.

With the turn of the century, the French were firmly entrenched. Saigon featured the best theater east of Suez, an array of palaces, a large cathedral, and all the other necessities of Parisian life. It was remarked that "nothing was wanting—except necessities." For the French masters there was the nightlife of the continent; for the peasants, squalid shacks, unending disease, lack of sanitation, and the antipathy and hatred of the colonial masters.

Prior to 1897, French policy had dictated assimilation which meant, in effect, suppression and destruction of the native culture. French law and French institutions supplanted native law and the family system of the countryside. Cochin-China, the oldest French possession, suffered most which meant an almost complete destruction of the existing institutions.

The French continued throughout this early period

to believe the grandiose descriptions of the merchant-adventurers, whose reports had been so influential in encouraging the policy of imperialism. By 1900 it was clear that the dreams were only dreams, that easier routes existed for the China trade, and that the southern provinces of China were, in fact, vastly over-rated as production and consumption centers. French interest now turned inwards, towards the exploitation of the land itself.

Policy towards the native population turned for the better with the arrival of Paul Doumer. Doumer had been a radical deputy and the Minister of Finance in the Bourgeois Cabinet; his assignment to Indochina was designed to remove him from the center of political life. He lasted five years, 1897-1902, reorganized the structure of colonial government, and gave it a measure of much-needed continuity. Cochin-China became a directly administered colony, Annam had a measure of direct control while remaining a protectorate, and Tongking was largely based upon self-governing community units. Control of economic affairs of the entire country was reserved to the office of governor-general.

The program of public works encouraged by the French produced an impressive set of statistics: twelve thousand miles of paved roads, six thousand miles of telephone, and twelve thousand miles of telegraph. But these improvements were used by the French and paid for by the Vietnamese. Taxation was brutal and the French colonial government exploited the traditional monopolies of salt, alcohol, and opium. In 1942, the monopolies alone accounted for more than sixteen percent of the total revenue, and of that amount, half came from opium.

The French established a university as early as 1904 and yet with a population of twenty million the student body was only slightly more than six hundred. In 1939 only fifteen percent of the school-aged children were receiving any education and the general population was more than eighty percent illiterate. The government promoted medical programs and education but there were only two Western doctors for every one hundred thousand Vietnamese.

For the working class wages were poor and conditions on the French plantations horrid. Despite growing exports and production, wages actually dropped. But the French colonial experience most directly affected the urban elite. They found little if any outlets for their talents and were the targets of scorn and derision.

It is not surprising that the French met resistance, both passive and active, during the entire tenure of their colonial enterprise.

The first major revolt against the French was organized even before the formal signing of the Treaty of Hue. In 1874, the "Scholar's Party" was formed and became the most powerful faction at the royal court. Several emperors were murdered for signing treaties with the French. After the French took possession a full revolt was launched in which twenty thousand were killed. The revolt died out in the 1890's.

The first important modern nationalist was Phan Boi Chau who, in 1906, organized the *Viet Nam Duy Tan Hoi* or Vietnam Modernization Society, which sought independence under a constitutional monarch. After the success of the Chinese revolution of 1911 and under the guidance of Sun Yat-sen, he organized the *Viet Nam Phuc Quoc Hoi* or Vietnamese Nationalist Party. While the society was not radical, it nevertheless trained many militants and organized a government in exile. Chau's career was ended in 1925 when he was delivered over to the French by the mysterious Nguyen Ai Quoc. The affair remains clouded. Some have suggested that the elderly Chau voluntarily gave himself up so that the reward money might benefit the cause

French soldiers at Dien Bien Phu.
(French Embassy Press)

while others hold that Quoc, a Communist, gave Chau up in order to be rid of his influence. Chau was first sentenced to death, but later this was changed to house arrest which continued until his death in 1940.

After the departure of Chau from the political scene, the *Viet Nam Quoc Dan Dang* (VNQDD) or Nationalist Party, was established. It grew during the twenties and in 1930 staged a poorly organized revolt. The episode ended with the execution of the party leader, Nguyen Thai Hoc, on a French guillotine; it is said that he died crying "Vietnam!"

By far the most successful activity against the French was that of the Communist Party. The story of the party's growth before and during World War II is the story of its most famous member. He was known under many assumed names but the last was his most popular: Ho Chi Minh.

Ho Chi Minh was born Nguyen That Thanh in central Vietnam in 1890. His father, a minor official during the period of the French intervention, vowed never to serve the colonial masters and gave his son his first anti-French feelings. Ho was in his early teens when he was expelled from a French school for his activities (although French historians suggest it was for his failing grades). For even an educated Vietnamese there was little opportunity and for a youth of known anti-French sentiment there was almost none. At the age of twenty-six, Ho decided to seek his future overseas and signed aboard a French liner as a mess boy.

He was a sensitive youth who found aboard the ship more of what he had left behind; wealth for the few and poverty and hard work for many. In France, and later in England, he supported himself by working numerous odd jobs. He shoveled snow for an English school. He then landed a job in the elegant Carlton Hotel, the center of pre-war English social life. But with the outbreak of World War I, Ho again began to wander.

He returned to sea, now as a mate on the dangerous trans-Atlantic run to America. In the United States he visited the coastal cities and observed American life first-hand.

With the end of the war, he returned to France where he was increasingly influenced by other men he had met and he was caught up in the post-war intellectual currents. He worked to organize the dispirited remains of the Vietnamese troops who had fought with the French and who were awaiting transportation home. But his first major political act came with the opening of the Versailles conference.

Ho believed in Wilsonian idealism and hoped that the men at Versailles could be induced to grant small concessions to the people of Vietnam. He prepared a list of requests for liberalization of French colonial policy and, carefully dressed in evening clothes rented from a second-hand store, took the commuter train to Versailles. He was ignored.

He supported himself in France working as a photo-retoucher and he gradually became more involved in left-wing politics and in particular the French Socialist Party. In 1920, he attended the Eighteenth National Congress of the Party where he begged the French radicals for a change in the policies of their country. Ho supported the line of the Third Communist International for one reason alone: its attitude toward colonies. He asked the well-fed socialists for more than words. The thin, intense Vietnamese was met with stony silence from the Frenchmen. That same year, he voted with the group which broke off to form the Communist Party of France.

His decision to join the Communists was motivated by the same concern that had moved him away from Wilsonian idealism and into the camp of the socialists: a deep sense of nationalism, a fierce desire to free his country from external control. So when Ho joined the Communists, he expressed little interest in polemics and ideology; his sole interest was in what could be done to establish Vietnam as a free nation.

Even his fellow party members found him too undivided and he was ordered to tone down his attacks on the French. Ho finally left Paris and went to Moscow where he worked at various meetings of the international Communist organizations. The time came to return to the Far East and in 1924 he arrived in revolutionary Canton.

The Canton of the 1920's was a melting pot set at boiling temperatures, and the man to watch was the dashing young Communist-trained commandant of the Whampoa Military Academy, Chang K'ai-shek. In 1925 Chang assumed control of the Chinese Nationalist Party and in alliance with the Chinese Communists, marched his army north to take the country back from the warlords.

In Canton, Ho organized the Association of Revolutionary Youth to advance the cause of revolution in Vietnam and established contact with the Communist machinery. But in 1927, when the victorious Chinese Nationalist Party armies reached Shanghai, Chang K'ai-shek decided the time had arrived to jettison his Communist allies, and this he did, sentencing all he could capture to death. Ho was forced to flee the country.

How now played a new and unfamiliar role. He had escaped to Thailand where he found safety in the Vietnamese colony. He donned the robes of a Buddhist monk and traveled about with the word of Marx rather than that of Buddha. But this life was too pastoral and Ho soon left again, this time to return to Europe.

The path of his wanderings is not exactly clear. He appeared at a Communist congress in Brussels and he visited Fascist Italy, worked in Weimar Germany, and found his way via the Trans-Siberian Railway across

Russia to board a ship for Hong Kong. It was in Hong Kong that Ho was arrested.

Security among the members of the Communist organizations in the Far East was never good, and Ho had been named as an agent. Moreover, France sought his extradition to Vietnam to face the death penalty. What saved Ho was the justice of the British government. Lawyers defended Ho's case to the highest court in England, the Privy Council, and there they won it. Ho was set free but he could no longer remain in Hong Kong so he went into hiding in Fukien province and later in the teeming city of Shanghai. In Shanghai he re-established contact with the underground and was soon shipped back to Moscow.

In Moscow Stalin now led the Communist world with his particular ideas. Ho was re-educated and received small jobs until the period of the prewar "popular front." It was the most painful of all of Ho's political trials for it called upon him to urge his comrades in the Communist Party in Indochina to work with, not against, the French. When the front was dissolved three years later with the signing of the Hitler-Stalin pact, the Communists who had been operating in the open were quickly rounded up and imprisoned. Ho was assigned to guerrilla activities, and for the first time in thirty years, he set foot again upon the native soil of Vietnam.

There, in caves in the extreme north, the ragged remains of the leadership of the Indo-Chinese Communist Party met. Japan was now the chief menace and France had fallen to the Germans. Ho calculated correctly that the Japanese would defeat the French and that they would in turn be defeated by the allies. Their plan was then to organize an underground which could step out at the end of the war as the single most unified and most powerful party.

With the fall of France and the coming of the Vichy

government, the colonial administration of Vietnam had pledged support to the axis cause. The Japanese demanded and had received the closing of the Tongking-China border, one of the few supply routes to Chang K'ai-shek's Nationalist army. But while the Japanese moved troops into Indochina, they did not assume direct control of the colony. The French administration became increasingly fascist and soon Vietnamese nationalists and Communists were joined in prison by French Jews and French Liberals.

In 1941 in the north, Ho and his followers had formed their front for a post-war government and it was named the *Viet Nam Doc Lap Dong Ming Hoi*, the League for the Independence of Vietnam, or as it was to be known and hated by the French, the Viet Minh.

With the war nearing its end, the Japanese suddenly moved to imprison the French colonial administrators and establish their own direct control. Bao Dai, the Western-educated emperor, was outside the royal city of Hue when the coup occurred. On March 9, 1945, returning to the city, he was met by the Japanese and offered the opportunity to declare the country free of the French. He accepted. Later he explained his action by stating that the French had failed to defend the country.

When Japan finally capitulated, the Viet Minh emerged and assumed power. Supported by weapons captured from the Thirty-eighth Imperial Japanese army, Ho Chi Minh, on September 2, 1945, declared the establishment of the Domocratic Republic of Vietnam.

The new government could not last without outside aid. A debate now ensued within Ho's cabinet: whether to seek aid from the Chinese or from the French. The left favored China but Ho told them: "You fools! Don't you realize what it means if the Chinese stay?

Don't you remember our history? The last time the Chinese came, they stayed a thousand years." He favored signing an agreement with the French to allow them to bring troops back and retain them in the country for five years. Ho said of the agreement: "I prefer to smell French shit for five years rather than Chinese shit for the rest of my life." The agreement was signed and Ho left for France to negotiate a final settlement.

The post-war French government was headed by General Charles De Gaulle and Ho hoped for an early settlement. He was given accommodations in a modest hotel, complete with a red carpet which stretched from the street to the door of his room. In the hotel he met another leader of a fight for independence and the two became friends. The man was David Ben-Gurion and Ho was so impressed by his description of the repression of the Jews and their fight against Britain in Palestine that he offered Hanoi as the site for an Israeli government-in-exile.

But Ho had his own problems as it became increasingly clear that the French had no intention of signing an accord. He made the decision to fight again.

On December 19, 1946, at eight p.m., all of the French power plants in Vietnam, carefully sabotaged beforehand, blew up. The country was plunged into the darkness of war.

The armies of the Viet Minh knew that they could not hold the cities and what little industry the country possessed but they did not have much interest in such a stand. They left the cities and returned to the country and the war quickly settled down to a war of attrition. Few decisive battles were fought and the Viet Minh sought to destroy, not hold, stationary positions. Ho wrote in 1947: "A pick stroke into the roads has the value of a bullet shot by our soldiers at the enemy."

As the war dragged on, the Viet Minh began to receive massive shipments of aid from Communist China

French paratroopers at Dien Bien Phu. (UPI)

and from Russia; the French received aid from the United States which eventually was paying eighty percent of the cost of the war. The tide was slowly flowing to the Viet Minh when a new French commander, General de Lattre de Tassigny, was appointed commander. He managed to inflict serious damage against the enemy but he died in 1952. Before his death, he planned and built a line of stationary positions which were meant to establish a defensive perimeter around the Tongking delta. It was a mistake. The Viet Minh filtered through men and supplies almost at will. And it created what was to become a fatal myth.

The tide of battle in 1952 was running for the Viet Minh. They had pushed up to the main French defenses. The French regrouped their forces around a small airstrip in the village of Na-San. The position was massively enforced and despite two regiments attacking it using the "human wave" technique, the fortress held. General Giap, the commander of the Viet Minh troops, was forced to withdraw.

Na-San was eventually evacuated but not before it had been declared a glorious victory. It was the most costly victory of the war, for it was the background for the battle of Dien Bien Phu.

Dien Bien Phu, like most great battles, was so costly and so absurd, that it should never have been fought. When it was over, ten thousand men, Viet Minh and French, were dead and the Communists held an insignificant village in the extreme northwestern part of Tongking. A small percentage of the French troops in Vietnam had been involved in the battle, but it so affected France that she was unable to carry on the war. Peace came soon.

Dien Bien Phu was born when the French command began to believe that stationary outposts could solve their major problem: how to draw enemy troops away from the front to defend their remote home areas. Na-

San had been won and it was suggested that Na-San could be repeated. A new French commander now arrived: General Henri Navarre, graduate of the French West Point, Saint-Cyr, who had been made a general at age forty-seven. He supported the plans and choice of the valley of Dien Bien Phu since it would conceivably shut the Viet Minh out of Laos. It could also serve as a base for behind-the-lines action.

Dien Bien Phu was fated from the moment the plan was conceived. The valley bottom which contained the few shacks which were the village was seventy-five miles in length and yet the French could only spare six battalions. Significant amounts of reinforcements would not be available.

The operation was named "Castor." On November 20, 1953, at 5:00 in the morning, an American-built C-47 aircraft took off from Hanoi's Bach-Mai airport. It arrived over the valley of Dien Bien Phu an hour and a half later. Its mission was merely to observe. Its crew consisted of three full generals and their staffs. The valley as they saw it was covered by a fog, characteristic of the area, but the fateful decision was made: the operation would be launched.

At 10:30, the first planes arrived over the valley where the observation plane was still circling. Dien Bien Phu was at that time occupied by the Communists and had been since the battle of Na-San. The Communist troops were undergoing tactical exercises when the drops began. The French were hindered in that men were separated from their equipment and dispersed over too wide an area. But the confusion also aided them for the Communist troops were unable to determine immediately the center of the drops.

At the end of the first day of fighting eleven were dead and fifty-two wounded. Exactly 1,827 paratroopers had landed in one day and the position was now considered secure. Ninety enemy dead were found on the battlefield but the bulk of the enemy troops had successfully made their escape through brush covering the Nam Yum River which ran through the valley.

On November 21, the second phase of the operation began with the dropping of the command post for the base and the second wave of troops. The French troops were now visited by the first in a wave of important personages–General Rene Cogny. He surveyed the operation and met privately with the base commander, General Gilles. Gilles had been the commander at Na-San and had spent six months boxed in by the enemy; he privately asked Cogny to transfer him at once. Cogny, commander of the northern theater of operations, promised that he would be.

The French troops now began the task of transforming the valley into a reinforced position. Daily aircraft runs from Hanoi brought in heavy artillery and supplies and, eventually, tanks. Meanwhile, the French began the offensive drives into the surrounding enemy territory that had been the object for which Dien Bien Phu was designed. The attacks were almost entirely unsuccessful. The enemy was well dug in and well concealed, and the French were cut to pieces.

After establishing the base at Dien Bien Phu, the French attempted to evacuate their base at Lai Chau, sixty miles from Dien Bien Phu. Over two thousand troops including thirty-four French enlisted men and three officers began the journey. When the remnants arrived at Dien Bien Phu, ten French men, including one officer, and one hundred seventy-five natives were accounted for; the rest were dead or missing and the Communists had captured enough weapons to arm a regiment. Within a few weeks, Dien Bien Phu was finished as a base for outside operations, the task for which it had been constructed.

The engineering officers at Dien Bien Phu were easily able to calculate exactly how much material would be needed to transform the base into a strong defensive unit: thirty-six thousand tons of various materials. After gathering as much of it as possible from all available sources in the area, there still remained a total of thirty-four thousand tons which would have to be brought in by plane.

To transport such an amount would have required twelve thousand missions by French aircraft but there were at most only eighty aircraft available. The engineering material alone would have required five months. The siege would begin in less than three months. And when it did and Dien Bien Phu was subjected to an almost constant artillery barrage, there would be protection for only the headquarters post, the communications center, and the x-ray room of the hospital.

The high command did not believe that the Viet Minh could transport heavy artillery through the dense jungle. Colonel Charles Piroth, commander of the French artillery, was convinced that his counterbatteries could spot and destroy any enemy artillery that managed to make it to the battle area. But signs of disaster began to appear.

Intelligence material showed that the Viet Minh were digging their guns into the surrounding hills in such a fashion that only the barrels were exposed. Moreover, rather then mounting the guns on the opposite face of the hills, they were carefully camouflaged on the side facing the French. The Viet Minh held the high-ground and a clear view; the French artillery was not dug in and the French had lost high-ground which could have been used for observation. When the battle opened the Viet Minh had over two hundred heavy artillery pieces and the French had sixty, of which less than forty were firing with any consistency.

Even more devastating to the French garrison would be the ability of the Viet Minh to supply their troops.

The French high command again accepted a myth—that constant air bombardment would destroy roads and bridges and hence prevent supply. But the Viet Minh responded by organizing thousands of coolies who, riding bicycles which could carry more than four hundred pounds each, traveled jungle paths impossible to spot from the air. The planes of the French failed to do anything more than slow the rate of supply of fresh troops and ammunition, while Viet Minh anti-aircraft guns effectively shut Dien Bien Phu off from the outside world.

On March 13, 1954, the Communist guns were continuously shelling the airstrip and rumors circulated that the attack would come that night. Enemy trenches were being laboriously dug at night and air photos revealed that they almost completely encircled the strongpoint known as "Beatrice," located to the northeast of the main camp. It was a well-fortified position defended by troops of the Foreign Legion.

At five p.m. the shelling began. Communist troops began pressing the outer defenses, and at 6:30 the command post took a direct hit killing the commander. Lieutenant Colonel Jules Gaucher, commander of the subsection which included strongpoint Beatrice, called an emergency meeting of his officers to name a new commander. As the officers gathered in his small office a shell penetrated the bunker and exploded. When the dust cleared two officers lay dying and Gaucher lay on the floor, his arms torn off and his chest open. He died in the arms of Dien Bien Phu's chief chaplain.

By nine o'clock the last message was received from Beatrice: not a single able-bodied officer was left and only small pockets of troops remained. The last message was for artillery fire—directly on the remaining fortification. The surviving men retreated from the hill by two a.m. and hid in the brush lest they be shot as the enemy if they tried to approach their own lines at night.

On Sunday, March 14, 1954, the Seventh Algerian Rifles, Fifth Battalion, manning the strongpoint called "Gabrielle," prepared for attack. Gabrielle was the strongest of the fortified positions at Dien Bien Phu. At eight o'clock shelling began: first 120mm mortars followed by 105mm howitzers. In the first few hours command posts were destroyed, radio sets knocked out—but the lines, while having to be drawn back, held. At 2:30 in the morning the attack ended. At 3:30 in the afternoon the next day the attack resumed. Again, a single shell found a meeting of the senior officers and rendered Gabrielle leaderless. The defense was longer than had been the case the night before on Beatrice, but by evening it was over and the French had lost close to one thousand men and their strongest position.

The next day it was clear that French artillery had not only failed to find and silence the Viet Minh artillery, but had itself been heavily damaged. Colonel Piroth, the artillery commander who had been so confident, now traveled to each command post apologizing
Machine 4 Day Shift 9-Caledoia 168 Dec. 4, 1970
for the failure of his weapons. He then returned to his own bunker where he lay down on his cot and pulled the pin of a hand grenade.

After the fall of Gabrielle, General Giap had tried more frontal tactics against the rest of Dien Bien Phu but the French held. Even with their limited strength and suffering terrible losses, they had been able to launch several counterattacks. With the beginning of April, Giap returned to those tactics which had brought him Gabrielle and Beatrice. It was to again be a war of attrition but this time the encircled French were to be even more tightly encircled. Trenches were dug surrounding each position and gradually these trenches grew tighter and tighter until they were only scant feet away. There was little the French could do to stop them; it was a kind of war for which they were totally unprepared. All they could do was wait, and listen each night to the sound of digging.

Supply problems became increasingly more difficult. Throughout the battle, the Viet Minh increased both the accuracy and the numbers of anti-aircraft installations. Toward the end of the battle, air supply could hardly keep up with the demand for ammunition much less that of food. Dien Bien Phu was never lost, it died a slow painful death from the day it had been conceived.

By early May the battle was over. The remaining troops were clustered in the center of the camp. At noon, on May 6, yet another surprise was presented to the French. The stillness of the clear afternoon was torn by the ear-shattering sound of rockets. Men died of asphyxiation as the sheer force of the blasts tore apart bunkers weakened by the rains. Troops who had never before heard rockets were panicked. The remaining arms depots were exploded and all of the medical supplies remaining in the hospital were destroyed.

At eight in the morning of May 7 the final attack began, first with artillery and then with huge numbers of infantry attacking the various remaining positions. One by one the various senior officers said their goodbyes to each other and then smashed their radio sets. Unit after unit was surrounded and captured.

It was decided that at 5:30 the garrison would cease firing. There would be no surrender. Shortly before the time arrived, a group of generals and journalists gathering in a small room in Hanoi heard the last message from Dien Bien Phu. The base commander, Brigadier General Christian de Castries, conveyed the decision to cease fire and said his farewells. "The transmitter shall be destroyed at 5:30. We shall fight to the end. Goodbye. *Vive la France.*" Five minutes later the transmitter resumed; this time it was the radio operator at the base: "In five minutes everything will be blowing up here. The Viets are only a few meters away. Greetings to everybody." The battle had ended.

The battle ended, the war ended, and the French adventure in Vietnam ended. In Geneva, at the League of Nations palace, on May 8, 1954, at 3:15 in the afternoon, French Foreign Minister Georges Bidault presented the opening statement. He haltingly delivered a brief note on Dien Bien Phu and of the bravery of its men. But one paragraph of his speech contained all there was left to be said: "We propose that the Conference should, first of all, declare that it adopt the principle of a general cessation of hostilities in Indochina based upon the necessary guarantees of security, the terms of the principles thus enacted being inseparable in our mind and in our resolution."

Only one day after the fall of the garrison at Dien Bien Phu, the French asked for peace. What had begun with only a few missionaries over three hundred years before was ended. The effects, the wound, might remain, but the French are gone.

CONTRIBUTORS

Neil R. Stout is an Assistant Professor of History at the University of Vermont.

George Stephens Clark is a freelance writer and historian living in Los Angeles. He is a former associate editor of MANKIND.

Angela Stuart, who authored five of the nine articles printed in this volume, is a prolific military historian and frequent contributor to MANKIND.

Lillian Morris and Philip Procter recently completed work on a novel set in Berlin during the last days of World War II. They authored "The Trail of Tears," which appeared in *The American Indian* book of this series.

Philip Finnley is a graduate of the University of California and studied at the Center for Chinese Studies at the University of Michigan.

THE HUMAN SIDE OF HISTORY

THE AMERICAN WEST